A Lord's Treasure

Book One Of A King's Wisdom

David S. Longworth

Edited By Elizabeth Sprinkle

A Lord's Treasure is a rudimentary personal finance book with the intention of also acting as a medieval fantasy tale. All events, places, and characters in this book are fictional. Any actual historical accuracy is entirely coincidental. Most, if not all, key financial lessons are italicized.

ISBN: 0999680900
ISBN-13: 978-0-9996809-0-2
eBook/Kindle ISBN: 978-0-9996809-1-9

To Theofanis Kakouras:

Thank you for inspiring me to walk the path towards success that I now stride.

~

To My Grandfather Wayne "Papa" Longworth:

Thank you for being an awesome grandfather and inspiring me to be a Christian man that can honor you and Nanny through achievement.

~

To My Grandfather Howard Vance Harrell II:

Even though I barely got to spend time with you throughout the twenty-two years of our mutual existence, I greatly miss you. Oftentimes I contemplate what lessons I could have learned from you, I wonder about what memories we could have made together, and how you felt knowing that your son, daughter, and all four of your grandsons are all inspired by your success as a businessman, in your local community, and as a loving father, husband, and grandfather.

~

To The Readers:

I greatly appreciate the love that you have given me by reading this book, the first book I have ever written, and I hope that you truly apply the knowledge within towards wealthier living.

CONTENTS

ACKNOWLEDGMENTS

I have learned a lot about the book writing and publication process during the challenge of successfully creating *A Lord's Treasure*. My thanks and appreciation goes out to my cousin and the editor of this book Elizabeth Sprinkle. She's been like an older sister to me since we were kids, and if she didn't edit this book for me then it wouldn't be nearly as good as it is.

PROLOGUE

The azure summer sky burns over Starkton, a kingdom on the continent of Lantheon, with insatiable heat, yet every person and animal persistently attempt to quench the heat's thirst with sweat and saliva. Men, women, and wealthy lords engage their errands and labor, while young children play; some dogs lie panting in the shade or near their adoptive humans; the livestock huddle into groups near the Healing Waters River which flows into the Titan Bay; and thirty cats scurry through the organized chaos and steal unattended food. To signify their respective social superiorities, the lords wear gilt samite and don a decorative pin over their heart, encrusted with gemstones possessing the respective colors and pin design of each of their families' coat of arms whereas the merchants prefer richly-pigmented velvet. Faint flowery scents coming from the nobility intertwine with a combination of the odors and aromas of sweat, manure, baked food, and mud filling the air.

Enduring the heat and various scents with duty, the Starkton sentries patrol the streets wielding spears, longswords, shields, and bows with arrow-filled quivers. They patrol on foot and horseback in the streets, rooftops, and near the river fully armored in steel and chainmail topped with an ivory surcoat emblazoned with a silver hare to symbolize that they ultimately answer to the ruling king of this region, King Gwayne Sterling.

Despite most of the lords choosing to walk through the city streets, Prince Drake Sterling, son of Gwayne, is being carried in an emerald-green litter by stout and bronzed servants wearing white hare-emblazoned tunics stained with sweat. Drake is a very muscular man with skin bronzed from outdoor constructive work, amber eyes, auburn hair, and black beard who serves as Starkton's Architecture Master after he succeeded upon the death of his predecessor Jolenta Bilteen. Jolenta is survived by her husband General Randall Bilteen and her four children Rickard, Robert, Marigold, and Colette. The lord-son Drake chose to wear his snow-white breeches and maroon shirt on this day to blend-in with some of the buildings in Starkton.

Drake's litter eventually stops at a small stone manor lined with white and orange dragon banners shortly past the hovels of the commoners. From the manor, a slender man in a samite sapphire and crimson doublet with black velvet breeches and leather boots with thinning and receding umber hair, silver eyes with violet flakes, short dark beard, and a crooked nose approaches Drake's litter. Two women sitting on a long bench near the manor's front door play a silver harp and a lute. The woman playing the harp is a thin woman with long, braided copper hair; silver eyes; and straight nose, who is wearing a worn lavender outfit with long-sleeves, leggings, and russet shoes. Her friend is a square-jawed woman with flowing marigold hair, purpureus eyes, and a gold and garnet fox pin fastened on her indigo dress. Sheathed daggers hang from both of the ladies' left hips

This has to be my destination since this man isn't dressed like those ignorant nobodies I just passed. "Good evening, I am Prince Drake Sterling, Starkton's Architecture Master and son of Gwayne Sterling, King of Starkton and Castellan of The White-Grey Keep. Is this dwelling the home of landlord Richard Wyvern?"

"Aye, you've come to the right place, milord. I am Richard, the woman with the harp is my sister Sable, and that's Marigold Bilteen." Richard Wyvern sports a grin full of crooked yellowing teeth and some gaps where some teeth used to be present.

Sable approaches and greets Prince Drake Sterling with "good evening, m'lord" while Marigold simply nods then returns to strumming her lute.

"I'm well acquainted with Marigold since I used to work with her mother." *I bedded Marigold too.* "It's peculiar that a man of your stature bears yellowing teeth, is missing teeth, and reeks of cat piss. At least your sister has the decency to have the scent of lavender about her, just like the color of her outfit unfit for a lady. I also noticed that you greeted me with 'milord' instead of using the proper address befitting royalty. Let's get your remaining teeth cleansed and get that godawful stench out of your clothing."

I've never thought about myself as a lesser lord before. Even though Richard and his siblings Abelot and Sable are baseborn yet their father's family, the Wyverns, have accumulated tremendous wealth and became one of the most prominent families in Starkton, Richard and his brother Abelot have been following their footsteps to continue this legacy by gaining riches and property. "Am I seriously going to be socializing with a member of the court and getting treated by them as well?"

"Indeed you are correct."

"So, am I *actually* going to enjoy the finale of this excursion, or are you simply 'seasoning the meat before the roast?'"

"There may be some roasted meat for you to devour with my father." Drake jokingly states "climb into my litter or I'll have my servants drag you into it, you reeking chamber pot." Richard stares at Drake with a blank gaze for twenty seconds then climbs into the litter.

During their trip to The White-Grey Keep, they pass a stone brothel; a wooden and stone brothel with its wood tinted snow-white and maroon called Alysse's Brothel that is frequently visited by the local businessmen and lords due to ownership by the queen; five smithies, which one of them is owned by Richard's brother Abelot and is named Abelot's Smithy; a hundred merchant stands; various wood and stone buildings used by other businessmen and professionals; and thousands of hovels. The density of the buildings gradually spaces out with more forestry and shrubbery along the path to The White-Grey Keep and other routes. The lords sparsely converse during this trip, but instead periodically look outside of the litter to view some of the scenery.

As they reach their destination, Richard Wyvern glares at a farmer walking past the litter pushing a wheelbarrow full of odorful cattle feces for fertilizer for agricultural usage. Richard then notices where the man was walking from, a gate and fence surrounding a meadow of tall grass and pathway to The White-Grey Keep, Starkton's stone castle with granite and white marble towers. The Healing Waters and Cook's Knife rivers, the two largest rivers within the vicinity of Starkton, flow less than a mile from The White-Grey Keep and into the Titan Bay.

As Prince Drake Sterling and Richard Wyvern's litter is traversing underneath the portcullis, a bakery, brewery, stables, servant quarters, castle guard and soldier barracks, and the grandiose oak and iron door of the castle's great hall become visible. *Ching! Ching! Shrung!* Sparring can be heard from the training grounds. Drake and Richard climb out of the litter after the trip, only for Prince Drake Sterling to briefly fall and get dirt stains on his snow-white breeches. They then proceed to enter The White-Grey Keep's great hall, a hall so elongated that raised seats stand on the left and right sides of the room, followed by two long white tables on each side of the hallway near the throne made of aspen wood, marble pillars with silver diamond patterns sprinkled alongside the central pathway and near the corners of the great hall, and a throne behind the tables that is elevated to overlook the tables and any visitors. This aspen-wooded throne has a curved seat, sheepskin lining the seat and back, silver hares dancing along the throne's head and large hares that make up the arms with their ears pointing backwards, and silver rabbit feet at the ends of the legs.

The great hall is empty except for Drake and Richard's presence. *Where on Earth is that fool of a father? Sleeping during the daytime again?* "Father?!" His voice echoes as if no one is anywhere near that area of the castle.

Stumbling into the room comes a pale plump man with shoulder-length grey hair balding on top, a thick grey beard on his reddened face, and one green and one amber eye, dressed in a diamond-patterned turquoise and black silk doublet with striped pants. He is wielding a flagon tipped over with a burgundy liquid steadily pouring onto the floor.

"My lord-father, do you realize that you are pouring wine all over the place again? Did you just leave the kitchen's wine cellar?"

"Yes, I just left the kitchen's wine cellar, and I am aware that I have poured this high quality vintage on the floor again, and I honestly don't give a flying feck, for I wish to enjoy the rest of my day. I AM THE KING OF THIS GOD-BLESSED CASTLE!"

"We're aware of that. Anyhow, I brought the one known as Ri-"

"YOU!" King Gwayne points at Richard. "Are you the one that the commoners gossip about in the streets; the baseborn son of

Peter Wyvern that jumped classes and built wealth for yourself alongside yer brother Abelot!?"

How does King Gwayne know all this? "Yes, Your Grace, I am the one that you seek. I am baseborn thanks to my lowborn mother and lesser lord father whom I haven't heard from in years."

Gwayne Sterling starts to smile, showing his whitened teeth, but his brow is furrowed. "Good. Since that's been clarified, I am now appointing you in charge of Starkton and The White Grey Keep's finances and mine own thanks to your accomplishments, Treasurer."

"Seriously? I never thought that I would be serving an honorable king such as yourself. Do you have anywhere that I can start with this assignment, Your Grace?"

Gwayne's facial muscles tighten, and eyes widen. He then proceeds to lean forward and retch near the wine puddle.

ONE: SAVING

An onyx sky slowly transforms into a cerulean welkin with a white-gold sun. Peach sunlight reveals the dust covering the furniture of the Treasurer's quarters. The morning sun blinds Lord Richard as he awakens with an excruciating headache, nausea, and the urge to urinate and defecate while visualizing a spinning room.

Even though I was appointed as the Treasurer of Starkton, The White-Grey Keep, and King Gwayne Sterling yesterday, my life currently doesn't feel any different; except I got five hours of sleep last night instead of my usual nine. Too much celebration and thinking about balancing my former life with this new one, but I think I will mentally and physically survive. Thank our battlemage-god Veritamor the squires and handmaidens knew how to clean up King Gwayne's puke or else I couldn't stand to have participated in last night's festivity in the

*great and mess halls and have my own room in this castle near the master
quarters and great hall.*

Richard Wyvern, completely nude, rises out of his bed that's
covered with wolf furs sewn into a blanket and a deer pelt bedding
cover shielding the hay bedding. He then proceeds to dress himself
in a rose-colored silk doublet embroidered with gilded paisleys and
pins a moonstone dragon pin near his heart, then slips into corduroy
breeches and black boots. All of his new clothes and moonstone pin
are gifts from the Sterling family and the guests of their last-minute
feast, which were mostly nearby liege lords and family members that
were present in other areas of The White-Grey Keep and in the city.
Richard's clothing from yesterday is hanging over the balustrades at
the balcony of his new room to dry after being washed late the
previous night by the handmaidens.

As Richard Wyvern begins to search the desk for the financial
records of The White-Grey Keep and King Gwayne Sterling, the
room is still spinning. Richard quickly sits in the oak chair to ease his
burden, but his attempt was unsuccessful. *Thump!* "Damn it!" His
head slams onto the desk and a red mark is left on the left side of his
face from the impact and his already crooked nose starts bleeding.
"Shit!" He plugs his nose with the ends of a nearby handkerchief
and continues searching for the books. The financial records were
underneath other books of entertaining literature and some letters,
some still with wax sealing, which the last occupant of the chamber
left behind.

How is this even possible? When analyzing the financial records of The White-Grey Keep, Richard Wyvern notices that there is barely any money recorded for the safe, but numerous entries of incomes and expenditures. There are no income entries in King Gwayne Sterling's book, but a tremendous amount of debts and expenses incurred. He records his observations.

Richard then gets up and rushes to the privy to relieve himself. The dizziness is lessened than earlier, but still problematic while Richard walks alternatingly swaying toward his left and right legs all the way back to his chamber. When he grabs the books and notes, he rapidly walks toward the master's quarters.

Gwayne Sterling's master chamber is large enough to cover the Treasurer's chamber ten times over, yet most of the space is filled with luxurious furniture and more than enough treasure to concern High King Lesirion about the possibility of unpaid taxes. Multiple brightly-colored rugs from the Elysium provinces line the floor. The walls of the room are lined with several animal skulls, book-ended by a pair of opposing, tall statues; one growling silvery wolf, perched on its haunches, and a golden, roaring lion with one ruby eye and an empty socket where another ruby must have once sat. A nude Gwayne Sterling is asleep in the bed with two nude harlots, which one is his wife Queen Alysse who owns and operates Alysse's Brothel.

"Your Grace? I hate to awaken you, but I must speak with you at once." Richard is staring to his lower right side, away from the nude women.

A Lord's Treasure

Why the hell would you bother me at a time like this? Can't you see that I was asleep and that I had company? Gwayne thought, but refused to say to his newly appointed Treasurer. "What the bloody hell happened to your nose? If what you have to discuss is as important as you claim, then I must tend to the business at hand. Ladies, out!"

Gwayne's pale-skinned wife Alysse, with curly auburn hair and jade eyes, and the olive-skinned lady with black hair got dressed as quickly as they could and rapidly left. Richard sat down in a nearby oak chair at the king's elm desk, placing the books down on the desk during the process.

"Nevermind my bloodied nose, I accidentally hit my head on the desk with dizziness earlier. Your Grace, do you have any knowledge about money and the maintenance of money? Did anyone ever teach you anything about it?"

Gwayne Sterling stares at him with his mismatched eyes, frowning lips, and wrinkled forehead. "Of course I know some things about money. I once read a book about it and I'm a bloody castellan of the most prestigious castle in this kingdom. Money defines who I am."

"Either you have been blind to someone possibly robbing you and The White-Grey Keep, or you don't know nearly as much as you think. You and this establishment are practically broke. Look at the numbers I analyzed and ran this morning." Richard retrieves the books from atop the desk and hands them over to King Gwayne.

As Gwayne Sterling sits upright underneath the bed covers and reviews the numbers in the books and parchment that had a brief overview of the situation, his face gradually gains more and more tension and redness. His face eventually darkens to a cabernet color.

"This is absurd. Have I really been this reckless? How should we begin to turn this situation towards prosperity, Treasurer?"

"We'll simply begin by saving at least one-fifth, rounded up to the nearest well-rounded hundredth, of all your incomes and those of The White-Grey Keep for your wellbeing and the wellbeing of The White-Grey Keep, respectively. Then we'll split that percentage in half to be diverted towards the castle's expansion and your retirement, respectively."

This goes against my dream where I gained financial knowledge. "I thought you were my Treasurer and not my Fool. This is folly. This is absolutely impossible. How will The White-Grey Keep survive and I live like I deserve?"

"It's not impossible. Much easier than you think. So easy that even the poor could do it without readily noticing their rising treasures. I follow this same principle."

"But how will I afford my Iytaleesh wine, trips to our capital Honet, brothel visits, clothing, and servants?"

"It's still possible to afford most of what you want and need, but please don't attempt to hinder the progress that I truly want for you and your people. In fact, saving ten percent of at least everything we currently have and receive can also make sure that we have plenty of soldiers and supplies."

Gwayne's mismatched eyes stare directly into Richard's eyes with disdain, then Gwayne decides to comment, "So be it, I'll try to find a way to meet halfway on my own expectations and your

12

expectations on behalf of my wellbeing and the wellbeing of The White-Grey Keep. Now, if you don't mind, I need to get dressed."

"At once, Your Grace." Richard then proceeds to leave the master chamber with the books and notes and search for a servant. He instructs a boy-servant no older than ten to find all of the highest ranking lords underneath Gwayne Sterling to instruct them to meet Lord Richard Wyvern in the great hall two and a half hours past noon. Richard returns the books to his desk and records notes for himself and those lords on paper.

Two and a quarter hours past noon have passed, and Richard sits upon the throne with his parchments while waiting for the next fifteen minutes to pass and the rest of the lords to arrive. Each lord gradually enters the room, slowly walks toward the tables, and then rotates their respective chair towards the throne. Tyrian Sterling, Naval Master and brother of Gwayne Sterling, who is wearing a phlox colored coat and a matching patch over his right eye while exposing his left amber eye, has a broad nose that is covered by a horizontal scar that curves below his left eye, long, wavy onyx hair with white streaks that extends to the top of his back's curve, and bears a steel cutlass holstered upon his hip. General Randall Bilteen, a stout, square-jawed man with grey hair fringed forward across his forehead, a thick rounded chin beard, and purpureus eyes just like his daughter's, and wears burgundy-painted heavy armor designed with a topaz fox on the torso and shoulder pauldrons and a falchion at his hip. Trade Master Deevon Yor, a slender, dark-skinned man originally from Pylon on the Canteenian Desert's western coast who has black eyes, a broad nose, thin black hair, thick black beard, has a curved kilij with a cobalt handle encrusted with emeralds on its quillons hanging from his left hip in an indigo scabbard, and is currently wearing a thin silk mauve and gold coat fastened with a golden lion pin upon his left breast. Tax Collector Sim Fostand, a scrawny pale man who wears a beige cotton tunic, pants, and hood to conceal his baldness, has brown eyes, a pointed nose, wrinkles from the early stages of being elderly and stressed, and carries a cinquedea blade at his right hip. Richard proceeds to stand after each lord is seated. Prince Drake Sterling has not arrived.

"Thank you all for gathering here today. However, where is Prince Drake Sterling? I have sent for each and every single one of you because I believe that you all are crucial towards my goals as the personal Treasurer of Gwayne Sterling and Starkton. The financial situation of The White-Grey Keep is not well, so it needs to be addressed. Effective as of immediately, one-fifth, rounded up to the nearest well-rounded hundredth, of all incomes is to be separated from the rest of the incomes and given separately."

Randall Bilteen curtly asks "Why are you planning to have one-fifth of all incomes separated from the rest of the money we receive on behalf of The White-Grey Keep? Embezzling it, just like your uncle Cedric, you little shite?"

"Absolutely not! I'm trying to fix the castle's situation at hand. Also, try to keep ten percent of all of your sector's incoming resources and total resources at their respective stations."

"We'll do our best to trust you, but if it turns out that you desire selfish intentions instead of honest deeds, then don't be surprised if you find yourself as grub for the dogs, just like your wretched uncle."

Richard Wyvern glares downward onto General Randall Bilteen with tension in his neck as the other lords switch gazes between them. Tyrian Sterling and Sim Fostand leave The White-Grey Keep's great hall while tension builds between Randall Bilteen and Richard Wyvern. Lord Deevon Yor glances at Randall.

"Now that I actually think about it, Randall, Richard's right to want us to set aside part of our incomes on behalf of the castle. He could use the expansion savings to more effectively improve everything about the castle and around the city while your sold-"

"I don't want to give up about ten percent of all the guards and soldiers on behalf of the castle when I can hit our enemies with as much force as needed," Randall irately hisses.

Drake walks into the great hall, with his yellow tunic and brown pants drenched with sweat. Sweat condensates upon his brow.

"General Bilteen, I promise unto you, Deevon Yor, and all the other lords and ladies of Starkton that you will not be negatively affected by having about one-fifth of your soldiers evenly placed aside and split between being designated as Starkton guards or extra reserve manpower. *Also, saving the fifth of all incomes and evenly splitting the percentage between reserves and expansion will only improve Starkton's economic situation over time. You'll quickly become accustomed to not having those incomes being readily disposable if they're reserved as soon as they're received."*

"Randall, just drop it and listen to him! King Gwayne hired him as our Treasurer so the financial situations for Starkton and Gwayne can be corrected and improved instead of getting worse," Deevon chimes. "I now understand why he wants this, for this tactic will work."

Randall stubbornly darts past Drake Sterling and storms out of The White-Grey Keep's great hall as Drake's eyes, then head, follow Randall with bewilderment.

TWO: EXPENSES

Four months have passed, two in a blazing summer and two during a bountiful autumn, since Richard Wyvern was named Treasurer of The White Grey Keep and King Gwayne Sterling. The drizzling skies are grey with dark cumulonimbus clouds. During the second month of Richard's tenure as Treasurer, a two hundred foot-wide moat with water flowing from the Healing Waters and Cook's Knife was built from ten percent of all incomes that were saved after Lord Wyvern held his meeting with the other high-ranking lords under Gwayne Sterling. Because the moat's construction requires irrigation from the Cook's Knife and Healing Waters rivers, the Sterling and Drake's channels were bent from the rivers and respectively christened after the most prominent family in Starkton as well as the Master Architect Prince Drake Sterling. The White-Grey Keep's moat is split by a two-foot thick granite wall forty-nine feet away from the castle's bank with a dam controlling the water flow of the other one hundred-forty-nine foot width. Water wheels extend from different areas of the castle's protective wall and rotate in the partition closest to the castle.

Richard Wyvern, peering over the ledge of a newly built chemise with its interior as a new wing of The White-Grey Keep, stares down at people fishing from the wider, cobalt section of the front of the moat. A person in a dark olive outfit with stains and second person in a stained russet doublet are seen racing horseback through The White-Grey Keep's barbicans over the footbridge towards the drawbridge. A castle guard faintly yells *"Open the portcullis! Now!"* Two lone ships traverse the Healing Waters River towards Starkton. Naval Master Tyrian Sterling, currently exposing his right bloodshot amber eye that he covers for sight while sailing in the darkness and using his left eye for daylight, approaches Richard Wyvern while barely making any noise while wearing his doublet made from ultramarine and purpureus Mesireen silk using shades unique to that province with faded black pants. He gazes at the people fishing below while standing beside Richard.

"Now that I think about it, I'm glad that you asked us to save twenty percent of all incomes and resources to separate away from the rest for The White-Grey Keep's wellbeing. Was all of this construction for the chemise with the wing, moat, and water wheels paid with *all* of the money? And why are you standing in the rain with no coat?" Tyrian turns his head to look upon Richard still admiring his work.

With whitened teeth, "Of course it wasn't. I only used a fourth of those designated incomes and some of the resources to fund this expansion, just like I promised King Gwayne. The rest was saved to have a plentiful reserve. Ironically, I actually spent much less than intended. And I wasn't intending to stand in the rain for an elongated period."

"How'd ye manage to reduce the expenses? This construction should've cost a lord's treasure."

"I simply reduced the expenses of the construction by finding ways to lower the expenses by meeting middle-ground between quality and quantity. Money needed to be spent toward increasing the castle's income from the citizens while also providing more protection for the castle and significantly reducing our expenses. *We need to reduce expenses where possible without causing hindrance or reducing our quality of life.* See those waterwheels?"

Both parties stare at the water wheels rotating in the rapidly-flowing periwinkle portion of Richard's moat. "Those waterwheels are connected to some mills that process much of the resources that we need. It was a necessary expense that saved an unspeakable amount of gold compared to the option of outsourcing the milling instead. It was a risky investment, but so far it's paying for itself."

"Does all of this work reduce some of our current expenditures?"

"Of course, since we needed some more guards for The White-Grey Keep and we simply transferred some of our laborers into castle guards and soldiers. They're currently still in training to ensure that they can protect the castle and its occupying lords, ladies, and citizens adequately."

"And what about *you*? How much profit are you getting out of the income?"

Richard stares into Tyrian's amber eyes with a gaze of disgust that transforms into sincerity after five seconds. "I honestly live off of the rental incomes that I receive outside of here instead of accepting tax money from this Treasurer position. Since your brother Gwayne is stubborn enough to still require me to receive an income from this position, I have agreed to only receive two gold coins annually. Now, if you will excuse me, I think we both should go inside and warm up."

Richard Wyvern begins to walk away, but just as he places two steps toward the doorway to his left side a ragged woman in unkempt, masculine clothing appears with a letter sealed with orange wax bearing the image of a dragon.

"Richard! Thank Veritamor you're safe!"

Richard stares upon Sable's drenched olive outfit stained with blood. "Starkton's been attacked, and Drake Sterling has been seriously injured."

Tyrian looks at Sable and Richard with a worried look upon his face as he says, "This isn't a joke, is it?"

Sable cries. "Why would I joke about something like this? Your nephew and my brother are caught up in an attack on the city! Marigold and I had to fight off some rapists! Drake's here at the castle also. I have this message here for Richard from Abelot."

A Lord's Treasure

Tyrian Sterling appears startled, and sends Sable away while wishing the best for her after she hands the letter to Richard. "Richard, I strongly suggest you open that as soon as possible. Don't let that woman's sprint to reach you go to waste."

Richard Wyvern opens the parchment with shaking hands. Richard reads the letter to Tyrian aloud. Richard vibrates. "...attacked by five-dozen catspaws in green clothing that suggests they're from a country of Canteenian influence. Lord Sim Fostand was killed by a catspaw that stabbed him twelve times in the chest, with one puncture to the heart, but fortunately Drake Sterling survived the attack with quite a handful of cuts. Some buildings were burned, and merchant stands flipped over. Farmers lost some livestock. Several of them raped civilian women. The dead haven't been counted yet, and I've seen no sign of General Bilteen anywhere. We're going to search their bodies and the ship that they came in to find out to whom they answer. Sincerely, Your Brother Abelot Wyvern."

THREE: SKILLS & EDUCATION

In The White-Grey Keep, King Gwayne Sterling sits atop his pale, silver throne accompanied by his royal guard and the Wyvern brothers. The hall is filled with merchants and common folk ready to receive the king's decree. Abelot's sapphire eyes stare out into emptiness while he stands calmly with his long, wavy copper hair laying on top of his dent-riddled gilded armor encrusted with chiseled moonstones that form a white dragon head upon the chest armor. Abelot's face is clean-shaven and his nose is crooked, just like that of his brother Richard. A bastard blade in its snow-white scabbard hangs from his back exposing a moonstone dragon head pommel, golden dragon wing quillons, and a crimson grip while a black scabbard is hanging from the holster on his left hip containing a rapier and is exposing the rapier's black handle encrusted with topaz gemstones and a moonstone dragon head pommel mirroring the one on Abelot's bastard sword. Abelot stares out into open spaces because he has issues handling excessive stimuli that utilize his highly delicate senses. The stench of body odor, smoke, and blood fill the room alongside the people that are in it.

Almost everyone is talking and rustling about. Tension has settled amongst the pandemonium originating from everyone's reactions except the guards trying to keep everyone civil, Richard and Abelot Wyvern, and Gwayne Sterling. Gwayne Sterling raises his hand to restore order to the great hall, and his attempt is successful.

King Sterling stares upon Abelot. "Abelot Wyvern, tell us of this incident and any information you have obtained as to whom caused it."

"Y-Y-y-y..." Abelot stops speaking briefly as a technique to improve his speech when he catches himself stuttering, which he often does. "Ye Grace, a-um galley entered the Titan Bay from the sea. It carried five-dozen p-p-people with dirks, scimitars, and s-swords on their-um waists. Her inventory was inspected, and as it was being inspected some of the voyagers had somehow walked away from the docks. When opening three of the v-vases, the dock workers found living Tavukish mountain vipers and sand vipers possibly from Pylon, which bit the dock workers and some of the citizens at the dock once they escaped the galley. While the few travelers remaining at the docks were confronted, scr-reaming started erupting along with those mercenaries drawing their swords. Many people died, and the streets are drenched with blood along with the damage they've done, but the assailants were quickly killed except for one of them that w-was captured for interrogation. General Bilteen was nowhere to be seen."

"He was here at the castle, training along with the soldiers. What of the evidence of these catspaws' origin?"

"When searching the ship, we located a book that was the ship's manifest and another we believe is the captain's log. It's being sent to Zenith Mountain University to be translated by someone at the university that can read it."

Richard Wyvern looks upon Abelot while standing near King Gwayne Sterling.

I wish General Bilteen would hurry up and get here already. "Thank you for the information, Abelot. As a general rule of thumb, I suggest that you should sharpen your skills in combat with our guards in training in the event that we go to war against whosoever caused this atrocity. Sharpen that bastard sword also. Morning Glory, was it? I'll try to do what I can to ensure we have the resources and funding necessary to prevent another attack and devastation that could ultimately lead to oblivion if unhandled."

"Yes, Brother, my blade is named Morning Glory. I brought your rapier Midnight's Arrogance with me since you *will* need it to protect yourself."

Abelot removes the scabbard at his hip containing Midnight's Arrogance, handing it forward to Richard. Richard removes the sword from the scabbard to inspect its condition. As it is exiting the scabbard, Midnight's Arrogance shines to reveal that its blade is jet-black with a topaz fuller and snow-white, wavy-patterned notches extending from the blade's shoulder to its point.

"Thank you for reporting this information to King Gwayne in a timely fashion *and* bringing me Midnight's Arrogance. If there is no more business to discuss, then we should probably send all of these frightened people back to their homes and wherever else necessary until we can get this mess sorted out."

Gwayne Sterling acknowledges Richard's statement, and raises his hand again. "Good citizens of Starkton, if none of you have needs to address, then please leave at once. Otherwise speak one at a time, starting where Abelot is currently standing. Abelot, you may go, I'll send for you if necessary, and I strongly suggest that you follow your brother's suggestion about training."

The merchants and some of the common folk line up to voice their complaints whereas eight-tenths of the occupants left the great hall, including Abelot. After leaving the odors and tension behind him, Abelot sits upon a stone bench next to some squared bushes in the castle's courtyard, watching the people leave while trying to get his brain to calm down after being exposed to too much stimuli at once. A woman walks by carrying some freshly picked rosemary for creating medicines and for cooking. The rosemary's aroma is strong. Abelot scowls at the woman until she hurriedly leaves his presence. Abelot's peripheral vision begins to blur. Sounds become louder. Eventually Richard leaves the great hall only to find Abelot yelling while he's repeatedly punching the soft, barely-grassed ground. Some common folk, a handful of lords, and laborers witness this incident.

Richard rushes to restrain Abelot and grabs him. "CALM DOWN, or else you'll break your hands again!"

After briefly restraining Abelot, his meltdown begins to simmer. Abelot then turns his head and looks into his brother's silver eyes as the violet flakes sparkle in sunlight.

"I'm sorry, Richard. It was everything around me again."

"You'll be fine. Now, since we both need to work on our swordplay, let us hone our skills in the training area."

The Wyvern brothers walk to the training grounds and wait for most of the soldiers to leave the training area before setting foot there. Richard finds some light leather armor to cover his torso, thighs, and shins on a nearby mannequin. Even though General Bilteen and some soldiers-in-training are still occupying the area, Richard and Abelot still find some room to spar. They unsheathe Morning Glory and Midnight's Arrogance. Morning Glory's bright indigo blade shines with so much luminosity that anyone not within close-quarters attacking distance cannot easily tell that it has a snow-white fuller with slanted crimson stripes lining the blade. Both the unique appearances of Midnight's Arrogance and Morning Glory were crafted years ago by a blacksmith skilled with creating high-quality metalwork and adding colors using various alchemical dyes, potions, and other ingredients while forging their metalwork.

Richard points toward Abelot's right shoulder above his breast, but Abelot simply swipes away the rapier's blade while wielding his bastard sword one-handed. Abelot tries to land a punch on Richard's right cheek, but Richard quickly retreats and taps Midnight's Arrogance's point near Abelot's navel.

He's good, but not fast enough. "One point."

Aggravated, Abelot wields Morning Glory with both hands while closing distance with Richard, smacks Richard's rapier away, kicks Richard on the inside of the bottom part of his left leg, then pushes him over as he bends downward toward his leg. Abelot smirks.

"One-one."

Richard picks himself up off of the ground. He quickly gets back into his battle stance, blade point aiming at Abelot's torso. Richard points the blade's tip at Abelot's right hip, feints the tip around Abelot's two-handed parry, then taps the tip on his right breast.

"Two-one."

After they put some distance between themselves, Abelot lifts Morning Glory with his right hand to swipe, only for Richard to point Midnight's Arrogance toward his left ribs. Abelot swings his arm while having his blade point upward to parry the blade near his hilt, then punches Richard on his right cheek with his left hand. Richard starts to bleed from his nose and mouth.

"Two all."

They salute each other, salute the spectators, then get back into position. Randall Bilteen stares upon the brothers with a surprised look on his face. As Richard is rapidly advancing towards

Abelot he starts extending, but Abelot is holding his bastard sword with both hands, crouches low to the ground, then jabs Morning Glory's point near Richard's navel.

"Three-one. I win. It definitely looks to me that I'm not the only one that needs to be training. *Working on your skills will not only make you better at what you can do, it'll make you more valuable to others who need your abilities, especially if you're offered compensation.*" The brothers shake hands.

All of the spectators, including an impressed General Bilteen, applaud the match since they were able to watch a bout as entertainment for once instead of simply preparing for battle.

"Indeed you are correct about the usefulness of skills and my bladework getting rusty. However, have you forgotten about the importance of education?"

Abelot stares at Richard's sweaty face with a confused look upon his sweat-barren face. "Education? Who needs education when you can simply live with only hard work?"

"I see that you've forgotten about keeping your mind as sharp as an executioner's axe. Read more books, especially ones that teach you new skills and knowledge that can help improve your abilities, wellbeing, and income."

Abelot and Richard Wyvern both attended Zenith Mountain University, a university that is located on the outskirts of Starkton five miles from The White-Grey Keep. Even though the brothers were both able to work for pay after graduation, Richard kept studying rigorously to maintain his current knowledge as well as learn new skills throughout the process whereas Abelot simply honed his skills in smithing and being a sellsword. Richard ultimately used his wisdom to improve his income through various income streams yet Abelot mastered being both a blacksmith and sellsword and increased his income significantly as well. However, Richard did lose some grasp on some skills while focusing heavily on improving others and learning new skills along the way.

"Abelot, I have forgotten to ask you something earlier. Have you learned any new skills over the past few years after we graduated?"

"I've been trying to perfect my skills with smithin' and fightin'. If anyone needs some high quality weapons and armor or some serious protection, I'm their blacksmith and sellsword. And yourself?"

"Carpentry. I'm also a landlord and now the Treasurer of The White-Grey Keep and King Gwayne Sterling in case if you've forgotten. I like learning new trades, it helps remind me of a lot of possibilities for living a meaningful life. I'm even investing in some endeavors I'm not willing to discuss yet."

"Are you sure that you could actually be successful juggling being the Treasurer, landlord, carpentry, and everything else you're doing?"

"I'll do my best to be successful. Even if I don't actually master the carpentry role and side roles, like you've been mastering smithing and fighting, I could always have carpentry be a productive hobby. I'm really good at being a landlord and Treasurer."

"Good."

The sky is a topaz void engulfing azure and indigo stripes with a motley pattern and the charcoal smoke billowing from The White-Grey Keep's bakery and smithy. After re-racking the light armor, Richard and Abelot grab some whetstones to sharpen their blades. Abelot sits on the ground and begins to sharpen Morning Glory while Richard sits on a nearby bench to sharpen Midnight's Arrogance.

"Congratulations, Richard. You fight pretty well for someone that handles numbers all day despite taking a beating." Richard quickly turns his bloodied head to the right and notices General Randall Bilteen as he walks over and sits on the bench beside Richard. Richard and Randall observe the training soldiers to ensure that their skills and combat intelligence remain sharp enough to be prepared for anything.

FOUR: INCOME

You're heading to *Fropilé?*" Richard asks.

"Yes, and I'm planning to return with a head or two," Abelot sharply responds.

Richard strolls away towards the populous of Starkton. Abelot directs four stevedores carrying two large oaken chests towards Captain Sterling's cabin and stevedores with five more chests downward into the storeroom through the hatch into the hold. They are all upon Davey Sterling's man o' war *Silver Hare*. Her hull's exterior is made of seafoam-stained aspen wood covered with rusting steel. Faded grey mainsails extend outward to resemble a fish's fins, yet the foremast has snow-white foresails that bear the silver hare of the Sterlings. *Silver Hare*'s ram is spiked within the inside of its curve. The silver hare of the Sterlings even leaps forward from the top edge beyond the forepeak as the figurehead.

31

Abelot contemplates the journey to Fropilé, a seaport metropolis in the province of Tavuk and how the implications of the journey could bring justice for the attack against Starkton and potentially ignite a war against the Etauq Empire. The captive that survived after the attack was harshly interrogated with bladed whips and stated that he and the other catspaws came from Tavuk, solely to "retaliate." However, a letter, alongside the books found on the catspaws' galley, was sent to King Gwayne Sterling from scholars at Zenith Mountain University trained in the art of comprehending various Elysium and Canteenian Desert languages stating otherwise. The letter identifies the ship as a merchant's galley named *The Water Phoenix*. The letter also states that the manifest and captain's log entries hint that the invaders started their journey from Pylon, stopped at Fropilé along Tavuk's coastline to better prepare for the attack, then continued sailing along the Elysium Sea and into the Titan Bay toward Starkton of Lantheon. Starkton was chosen because the kingdom has been a major trade partner with provinces within the Etauq Empire, most notably the island provinces Pañase and Iytal, the seaside metropolis Mesir of the Canteenian Desert, and Tavuk after the Etauq Empire conquered most of the continent Gany and its surrounding western islands.

Abelot leans upon the railing toward the docks to gaze upon the recovering Starkton. Construction laborers are rebuilding the destroyed buildings and doing repairs. A new necropolis is being cleared from some of the rubble of where a few edifices once stood near the largest marbled chapel in Starkton, Verítamor's Blessing.

Dum! Clang! Dum! Clang! Verítamor's Blessing's carillons vibrate during service. Citizens dressed in the respective styles of their social class conduct their business while the stevedores prepare Tyrian's man o' war *Silver Hare*, the invaders' galley *The Water Phoenix*, and eight frigates for sail to find those responsible for coordinating the recent destruction and death. Abelot turns around only to find Captain Tyrian Sterling in his silver surcoat standing behind him.

"Boo! Scare ye?"

"No." Abelot moves his eyes to his lower right for half a second. "I'm too concerned with all of this going on. Could there be another attack after we leave? Will we start a-a war? What's going to hap-pen with… with our trade routes with the Et-tauq Empire? What happens if we're wrong?"

"Don't think about it like that. In fact, don't even sweat this. My brother gave me the books to use as evidence to present when doing the confrontation, so it should turn the meeting in Fropilé in our favor. We'll be doing some trading along the way to make some money."

"Where at?"

"Fropilé, of course. You didn't think we were simply getting ready to confront a potential ally with this problem and also not think about gold, did ye? We have obligations to fill and standards to meet, especially since I'm Starkton's Naval Master. These ships are carrying a broad and deep variety of goods from the merchants to trade."

As the conversation continues, Richard arrives with Deevon Yor, promptly approaching Tyrian and Abelot with the gilt threading of Richard's emerald-green doublet dappled with golden diamonds and Deevon's marigold doublet illuminating prominently under the autumn luminescence.

"Good evening, my lords. Are the ships ready for trade?," Richard inquires.

"Almost."

"We'll still need to review the manifest before you both leave for Fropilé in Tavuk," Deevon remarks.

"Good. Also, make sure that you both bring Starkton Trade Company the best possible profit. The Wyvern fam-"

"What?! You and I are also responsible for these goods being shipped!?" Abelot exclaims with shock.

"Brother Abelot, did you not hear through gossip that I recently acquired Starkton Trade Company, which provides logistics brokerage services to the Starkton shipmasters and merchants? You'll get some income too, for supervising the logistics alongside Tyrian, of course."

Deevon states "indeed Abelot, your brother has made this acquisition with me acting as witness for the sale closure."

Richard, Tyrian, and Deevon stare at the shocked look upon Abelot's stubble-bearded face.

"T-This is news to me. Are you sure that you could still try to hone your carpentry skills on top of everything, and this too?"

"I think I will most likely treat carpentry as a hobby that I can use to sometimes earn extra money. Before I forget, I also have an interesting proposition for you on behalf of Queen Alysse. Come with me now."

The Wyvern brothers start walking away from the ship, with Captain Tyrian Sterling following them.

"Please don't follow us. Have you forgotten about Deevon's implied mandate?"

Tyrian Sterling briskly nods with a darkening face, then returns to his duties by conversing with Trade Master Deevon Yor with the fleet's manifest in hand.

Abelot and Richard continue walking towards Starkton from Titan Bay's wharf, on White Dragon Street heading northwest, which was renamed from Jester's Fumble in honor of the Wyvern siblings' father Peter and uncle Cedric, before Cedric's downfall. Peter Wyvern was renowned for owning houses that he rented to the people of the metropolis while Cedric oversaw the wellbeing and improvement of Starkton's sewers; Peter and Cedric, for five years, also owned a shipping company that mostly dealt with transporting goods by land.

During Abelot and Richard's walk, they dodge falling excrements from people dumping their chamber pots out of their windows as beggars line the streets begging unto the common folk, receiving free handouts from some people and insults from others.

"Well, brother, what is it that's so important that you wanted me to follow you into town on our forefathers' street?"

"See that brothel over there?" Richard points at the building of the prestigious Alysse's Brothel. "We need to visit it."

"Both of us, at the same time?"

"Both of us, at the *same* time."

The brothers approach the brothel, Alysse's Brothel, where most of the visitors are nobility. It's a large snow-white building with maroon exterior wall bracings, with its lower sixteen feet encased in jagged stone walling. The structure is large enough that it could serve as an urban military encampment during the event of an invasion or civil war. White hares are engraved and stained upon the entrance's maroon casing.

As Richard and Abelot enter Alysse's Brothel, the aroma of mint is overwhelming, more than some faint coital moans. A five feet tall marble statue of a man and woman kissing stands upright in the center of the front lobby, surrounded by multi-colored sitting furniture occupied by men and women speaking with each other while some people kiss. Abelot's sapphire eyes follow two gorgeous women walking past the Wyvern brothers. Most of the people visiting this brothel are finely dressed lords, merchants, and a few ladies. Many elm-wooded doorways for rooms line the mauve-tinted walls, both on the main floor and on each upper level, with an elm stairwell at the back left corner of the building that rises upward and rotates in a short radius. Sepia tables holding vases and knick-knacks line the walls while crushed mint rushes cover the stone floor.

An olive-skinned wench with wavy dark hair approaches Richard and Abelot wearing a citrine-yellow thin dress with black silhouettes of lions that accentuates her cleavage. "Good day, sirs. My name is Crystabella. Would you like to know about us and our pricing so you can make the best choice?" Her almond eyes stare directly at Richard Wyvern head to toe. "*You* look familiar." A beautiful white smile, not missing any teeth, enters and accentuates her flawless face.

I know I've seen her before. "You seem familiar also." Richard thinks for ten seconds. "Oh yes! Last time I saw you, you were with Alysse and Lord Gwayne at The White-Grey Keep!"

Crystabella blushes. "Oh yes, I remember that day now, and most definitely the night before. What was your position again? Treasurer?"

"Yes, I am the Treasurer of The White-Grey Keep and Gwayne Sterling. Also, we're here to speak with *Alysse*. Tell her that Richard Wyvern is here *with* his brother Abelot."

"As you wish, but I think I should say *handsome* brother Abelot." Crystabella walks into a room near the entrance.

Oh, the things I would do to her and those two earlier. "What's this about, Richard?"

"Good evening. Was someone looking for me?"

Both men turn around to find Alysse Sterling in her magenta gown partially covered by her lustrous auburn hair.

"Good day, Queen Alysse. This is my brother Abelot. We're here to discuss investment in your establishment."

"Oh yes, Richard. Come with me into my office."

Abelot, Richard, and Alysse walk into her office. Alysse closes the door as Abelot and Richard sit in oak chairs, then she takes seat behind her oak desk.

"We want to invest in your business. How much would ten percent of all profits cost us upfront?"

"Eighty-five thousand gold."

"Eighty-two thousand is what the Wyvern family can offer."

"Done."

Abelot turns to Richard. "Richard, how can this be fair to her? Doesn't she have to work for her money?"

Alysse smiles at Abelot. "No, handsome. I don't have to work for my income from this brothel. I do *sometimes* work for extra cash, however, and my husband and I benefit from it."

Richard chimes, "Abelot, with passive income streams, we can build an unimaginable amount of wealth in relatively short time. *We can build passive income streams from business ownership, collecting rent, writing books, writing plays, and numerous other methods.*" Abelot stares between Richard and Alysse with a blank stare. "Thank you for this interesting investment opportunity, Your Grace. We look forward to this exciting new experience."

"Abelot, your brother is right. Does my family have to work? Of course we don't since we have so many passive income streams, but we do work as needed."

Abelot stares into Alysse's jade eyes with disdain. "It doesn't fe-feel, um, right. I've almost always worked f-for my money."

"Now that you know a piece of the truth about building wealth, you can correct that prideful, misconstrued principle over time. It can differentiate the opulent from the impoverished, and make the rich more affluent."

A Lord's Treasure

The Wyvern brothers stand up, nod at Alysse, and then leave her office. Crystabella approaches them on their way out.

"Hey Crystabella, Abelot's going to be traveling to the Elysium for a while."

Richard gives her a small sack of coins.

FIVE: RISK MANAGEMENT

Storm waves smash against *Silver Hare*'s hull while Abelot struggles to sleep in his cot in Captain Sterling's cabin. Squalls and gales scream as rain feeds the Elysium Sea south of Pañase's coast. Abelot is pale and sweating. Nauseated from each wave's excessive force, Abelot arises from his personal cot and walks over toward an opening to look at the other ships and retches out the opening. Only one frigate and *The Water Phoenix* can be barely seen amongst the darkness and rain. Lord Tyrian Sterling relaxes in an emerald outfit on his cot as he continuously studies the details regarding the journey. Numerous lit lanterns show the organized nature of the cabin Captain Sterling and Abelot share. Abelot's boots and gauntlets lay on the floor next to his cot.

A Lord's Treasure

I wish I could be with Crystabella right now, staring into that tart's beautiful almond eyes as I make love with her again. "These waves are t-t-t-too harsh for the sh-ships and my stomach-ach. How many do you think we'll lose?"

Tyrian looks up at Abelot, who is covering the bottom half of his torso armor with his hand where his gut is located.

"Hopefully we'll not lose any if the captains have the smarts to manage the storm tides well. Also, don't lose your repast in here. Why do you oftentimes wear that particular set of armor instead of wearing better armor, or even actual clothing? I thought you'd be wearing something more comfortable to sleep in instead of your armor. Relax."

"Crystabella at Alysse's Brothel could help me relax. I've had this armor for a long while. It's saved my life numerous times, from simple brawls with unhappy customers to wild animal attacks to *even* idiots desperately failing at ending my life."

Tyrian smiles. "It obviously can't protect you from the females though. You don't have to be an idiot to start a fight with someone such as yourself. Some people prefer a challenge." Tyrian Sterling picks up his hare-engraved silver kukri dagger and starts flipping it through his fingers. "I heard your brother gave you some competition when you both trained together back at Starkton."

"Yes, he's definitely skilled at fighting with a rapier. I don't know how he'd fare using longswords, bastard swords, and great swords though. I'm glad that he still knows how to use a sword at least. Things might start brewin' when we confront this Septimius person or whichever pompous shite orchestrated this mess."

The screams from the squalls are deafening. The lights become blurry. The cabin has a strong musty odor. Abelot's insides burn with excruciating pain. *Kirsch!* Abelot falls to the floor flailing his limbs violently with uncontrollable anxiety and primal rage. Captain Sterling jumps off of his cot and rushes to calm Abelot. Abelot growls as he swings his arm at Tyrian.

"Abelot! What the hell?!"

Abelot growls while staring at the ceiling with a deadly gaze.

Tyrian Sterling puts out a few of the lanterns. Abelot's growling becomes softer and his body movements also soften and slow. Abelot slowly looks upon Captain Sterling. *Damn all this shit!* Tears fill his ghastly sapphire eyes.

"I'm s-s-sorry, Capt-t-ain. I have *brain* problem-m-s. Too much happening at once."

Tyrian stares into Abelot's marine eyes. Tyrian's facial muscles release tension.

"I appreciate you letting me know. I bet it's difficult sometimes," Tyrian states softly.

"Y-yes. I don't like crowded places, loud noises, strong odors, too much a-t-tention to spr-r-ead."

Tyrian assists Abelot towards regaining his composure. Tyrian then lies back onto his cot. Not a word is stated between Abelot Wyvern and Tyrian Sterling as they try to relax in the dimly lit cabin. *Gurgle. Gurgle.* Abelot then rushes toward the window and regurgitates outside again onto the side of *Silver Hare* and into the Elysium Sea. His forehead burns with fever. He then returns to his cot, lies down, nods into unconsciousness.

That squally night Abelot dreamt a fever dream. Abelot oftentimes has nightmares that occur for months at a time, yet occasionally has pleasant dreams. A woman with a straight nose, no mouth, braided umber hair, and silver eyes that almost match her granite-grey hooded tunic, breeches, and shoes stands behind a sandy-brown stone castle in a field of barely-grown grass and dying grass below a bright purple sky mottled with long, skinny magenta cirrus clouds. Orange sunlight reflects off of her steel dirk and onto the onyx scabbard of a rapier holstered upon her left hip. Her rapier has a black handle encrusted with topaz gemstones and a moonstone dragon head pommel. The woman turns toward Abelot, who is standing several feet behind her. A pink mouth with a flat upper lip reveals itself as the woman turns toward Abelot.

"We need to strike when the sky darkens. Remember, Cedric Wyvern is our target. Kill only as needed."

Abelot stares upon the transmogrified woman and notices familiarity. "You look familiar, and so does that rapier at your hip. Why are you trying to kill my uncle?"

"Your father paid us since he needs to remove your corrupt uncle, My Bastard Abelot."

That was when Abelot understood everything. Now that he truly recognized this catspaw as his deceased, abusive mother Winifred Catrain, he was able to identify her rapier as Midnight's

Arrogance. Abelot, Sable, and Richard were not titled with the
surname Catrain at birth because Winifred and their father Peter
Wyvern insisted and were granted by the monarchy that his last name
should be continued even though the children were bastard-born,
especially since Winifred falsely loved them. Abelot heard rumors
when he was a boy about the assassination of his uncle Cedric, a man
who caused a riot in Starkton after he invested most of his family's
money towards building five heavily fortified wagons to transport the
merchants' goods by land only to have them raided and destroyed by
thieves. Cedric spent the remainder of the shipping company's
budget on importing fine Iytaleesh wine and other goods for himself
by sea instead of on skilled mercenaries to protect the caravan. He
also committed heinous crimes against his family and unto numerous
others throughout his lifetime.

Darkness suddenly consumes the dusking sky. While the sky
darkens, faceless sentries wearing russet armor bearing the white
dragon of the Wyvern family position themselves at all openings for
the castle while eyeless archers take point atop the castle's ramparts
and bastions. Torches are lit along each sixth castle crenellation, with
one in each corner of every bastion. The castle's keep is well lit
compared to the windows of most turrets and brattices. Some
barrels and crates lay disorganized near the passages.

"Abelot, how do you suppose we will enter the castle?"

"I think you should find some bricks and corbels jutting out
of the wall to climb upward and open the rear portcullis for me."

Winifred searches for some bricks and corbels jutting outward, but does not see any. She instead creeps towards the guards with Abelot close behind. They each pick a guard, and then silently slice their throats to the bone. Abelot then takes one of the guards' armor to disguise himself while Winifred hides in the shadows as best as possible. Winifred sacks up Abelot's armor and hides it within a nearby barrel. Abelot searches for a nearby guard, and then suddenly one appears. The guard stares at Abelot.

"Hey Edric, where's Walder?

"He went to piss a few hours ago but never came back. I couldn't find his torch nor him when I stepped away from the gate looking for him."

The guard, unknowing of the situation, opens the portcullis to speak with Abelot to help him search for a guard named Walder. Just as soon as the guard steps outside the portcullis and notices the maroon earth where Walder and Edric were slain, Winifred swiftly ends his life by piercing him through the back of his neck. Both Abelot and Winifred slip in and close the portcullis behind them.

As they enter the castle, no guards seem to be patrolling the central courtyard. Banners that have orange fields with a white dragon, the official banners and sigil of the Wyvern family, hang along the castle walls.

Winifred rotates her head towards Abelot. She whispers, "We should split up. I will check the southwest while you check the northeast. That wretch has to be hiding somewhere."

"I don't like the look of seeing absolutely no guards. Could they be waiting for us?"

"We'll find out soon enough."

As Abelot and Winifred part ways, Abelot passes a few guards within the castle keep's interior. He subtly nods at them when they acknowledge his presence, but he doesn't say a word. Eventually he finds an aspen-wooded door engraved with silver hares and burgundy foxes.

"Is this where my uncle Cedric is hiding? Why is this place symbolizing the Sterling and Bilteen families' influence?"

Abelot stands outside of the door contemplating what he sees, but when his thoughts quickly become erratic, the hares and foxes disappear. The door suddenly disappears, flying away as tiny white dragons and simultaneously scurrying about as burgundy foxes and silver hares. Winifred Catrain appears unto Abelot with her clothing and Midnight's Arrogance drenched with blood. They both enter, only to find a bald-headed man with violet eyes, thick dark mutton chops, and orange armor encrusted with moonstones forming a dragon on the cuirass sitting at a large desk with treasure all around.

Abelot immediately unsheathes Morning Glory and points the tip at Cedric. "Cedric, tell me why you're leading our family name through dirt and why you committed your crimes."

"You idiot bastard! How did you reach this place without being slaughtered by my personal guard?" Cedric's face is tense, yet the rest of his body appears calm. "That was hasty of me, I'm quite impressed you and this harlot made it past my guards."

Anger takes over Winifred's face. Winifred growls, "I found most of them drunk in the mess hall, passing around the kitchen wench. I killed them for sport. Even if you wanted to call for backup at this time, no one can save you from your demise tonight. Have you forgotten that I love your brother Peter and mothered your niece and nephews?"

"I could never love any of his whores or a bastard nephew. I should have slit Abelot's throat after I-."

"You're nothing but refuse, Cedric."

Cedric stands with his longsword in hand, revealing that he actually had it laying in his lap the entire time. Abelot unsheathes Morning Glory with both hands.

"My siblings and I may be baseborn bastards that were ultimately given our father's surname because my parents begged for it, Vileness, but we're more honorable than a man that betrays those who trust him for his own selfish gain and evil intention. I protect the weak with my sword and making armor and weapons, unlike you. I am a white dragon in this world of darkness, killer of evil. Prepare to die."

Cedric swings his longsword in the air, only to miss Abelot as he quickly squats. Before Abelot can stand up again, Winifred rushes behind Cedric and stabs him in the armor gap under his right arm. Abelot rams Morning Glory through Cedric's skull as he stands upward, only to hear him repeatedly screaming.

This isn't possible, Abelot thinks in shock. *My sword is through his skull.*

Abelot suddenly awakens to find Tyrian Sterling yelling out the cabin door at the mariners. Abelot quickly puts on his boots and gauntlets and rushes onto the deck. Chaos is erupting upon *Silver Hare*'s deck, with white fog surrounding the entire fleet. All of the ships, including *The Water Phoenix*, are surrounding some smoking wreckage. "What's going on, Captain?" Abelot asks as he stares at all of the people crowding together.

Tyrian's expression shows stern. "Ab, we've caught a pirate that attacked our ship alongside some other pirates. All of the other pirates with him on that brigantine died when we awoken and discovered their presence. So far it seems that only one frigate was sunken while we slept. Her cargo was stolen, and presumably hauled off by a schooner flying the Pañase standard that was spotted sailing west towards Pylon. *The goods will be gone before we can catch them, even if the wind blows in our favor.* The idiots sailed their single brigantine towards *Silver Hare* after sinking the frigate, so all of our remaining frigates and *The Water Phoenix* surrounded them and attacked with catapults tossing flaming pitch unto their hull. Most of them died quickly, but the rest were stupid enough to board *Silver Hare* to escape drowning and we mercilessly slaughtered them all but this one. You and I actually slept hard, since we both missed the battle."

I had a battle of my own last night. "Goodbye to your plans for successful commerce since that frigate's goods are gone."

"Not necessarily. *We split each merchant's cargo amongst each ship in case something like this happens. Risk management. We've probably lost only ten percent of our goods and men instead of risking a higher percentage by having all the cargo, or a particular merchant's cargo, on one particular ship.* We can drive up the prices to try to recuperate the loss."

The captured pirate with a crudely-cut brown beard and tattered clothing is tied to the foremast by *Silver Hare*'s shipmates.

"Abelot, do you want the honor of interrogating this punk?"

"This isn't for honor, but instead for justice."

Abelot rushes over to the pirate and punches him in the ribs. The pirate lets out a yell as his mouth begins to bleed.

"Who sent you to capture our cargo and goods?"

"Feck off, ye twat!"

Abelot, with a blank yet deathful glare, punches the pirate in the jaw while wearing his gauntlet. Blood and teeth fly out of his mouth.

"I'll ask you nicely again. Who, the hell, sent you to capture our cargo and goods?"

"Feck off, ye sword-swallowing bastard!" The pirate spits blood onto Abelot's armor.

Abelot looks over at the crewmembers and says "pull his pants to his ankles." "Tyrian, I need your dagger. Let's teach this little shit a thing or two about life without *his* sword."

Tyrian hands Abelot his dagger while the crewmembers pull down the pirate's pants, exposing his penis and testicles, while blood runs down his face and onto his ragged shirt.

"WAIT! It was a skinny woman with a *green and gilded* hooded cloak in Fropilé! Gemstones in her dagger and bow! Please don't make me a eunuch!" Tears fill the pirate's eyes.

"Thank you for your honesty. Don't worry, we're not going to castrate you. However, your leader put too much trust in you and doesn't know how to manage risks. *I'll take a risk of my own and let Veritamor decide your fate.*"

Abelot grabs the pirate by his left shoulder then carves his chest all over. Blood gushes unto Abelot's armor and Silver Hare's deck. The sailors drag the bleeding pirate while he paints Silver Hare's deck sanguine and toss him overboard towards the wreckage.

SIX: MENTORSHIP

Seagull squawks and harmonious voices fill the tepid autumnal atmosphere of Fropilé's wharf with accord and verve. Whitened daylight disconnects existence from perceived emptiness. The stenches of body odor, marine life, and saltwater blend within the atmosphere around Abelot Wyvern as he and Naval Master Tyrian Sterling supervise the stevedores and shipmates carrying the goods for trade into Fropilé. *Grraaawwrr////!* Six caged wagons bearing a banner with a green dragon on a golden field carry green-armored gorillas. *One month* has passed since Abelot and Tyrian sailed from Starkton to Fropilé. Abelot did not shave during the expedition, but instead let his beard grow. Despite Fropilé having many shops for bartering throughout the red and yellow clay city and near the dock, Fropilé's primary income centers are the Ruby and Emerald Bazaar, which got its name from the rubies and emeralds that adorn the structure, and the brothels scattered throughout the metropolis.

Even though there are many brothels all about, a gargantuan twenty-towered basilica with a maroon, ivory, and citrine exterior; domed roofing; a small tholos encircled with oculi at the top of the tallest tower; and at least forty arched and stained windows is visible all throughout Fropilé a mile northeast from the docks. The church was erected by the zealous Fropilé architects under direct command from Emperor Septimius to remind the citizens of the significance of Verítamor's presence in everyone's lives, whether or not the people actually serve this god.

While studying the city from the docks, Abelot spots the emperor's palace a mile north of the basilica near the northeast border of Fropilé. The emperor's palace is an enormous gold, snow-white, and purpureus-colored structure with two buildings that both have a hundred pillars surrounding the ground level with some adjacent to the balustrades on their upper levels overlooking part of the Verítamor's Vow plains north of Fropilé. A tholos just like the one on the basilica is present atop the palace's main wing and the secondary wing. The emperor's palace yard is surrounded by a fortified rampart, yet the secondary wing of the emperor's palace stands northwest of the main wing and has a gated walkway under a balcony perpendicular to the guard wall.

Tyrian points at the two-wing building with a drooping gilded black sleeve. "Abelot, the Regemarce north of Fropilé's basilica Verídom is where we need to go to get the attention of Septimius and confront him about the attack on Starkton and on our voyage, but I think we may need to find an official to properly introduce us so he won't think to send *our* heads back to Starkton instead of *us* bringing back the heads of the facilitators. Please go find someone while I supervise the stevedores and our crewmates."

"Are you sure that's the correct building, Lord Sterling? Both buildings look significant to me."

"Aye, I've sailed here before. The basilica's called Verídom and the palace is the Regemarce. The Regemarce's secondary wing is the Royal Library."

"Thank you for the information. I'll keep it in mind when searching for a lord to help us."

Abelot ventures out from the wharf bearing north towards the Ruby and Emerald Bazaar. Along his path to the bazaar Abelot notices the numerous shops, dwellings, brothels, and chapels that define the populous on either side of the russet stone pathways. An older bronzed woman with a grotesquely deformed pointy right shoulder wearing an emerald scarf and plain full-body mantle walks past, followed by two green-armored guards. When passing a smithy near the Ruby and Emerald Bazaar, raggedly-clothed blacksmiths with low quality equipment stand nearby their shop and try to solicit Abelot to request their services due to his dented gilt armor, but he refuses their "deals" with hardened fortitude. As Abelot reaches the marketplace, more and more ornately outfitted persons coat the streets, only for Abelot to be surprised when he realizes that very few of them were truly upper class.

Abelot finally reaches the Ruby and Emerald Bazaar, only to experience an implausible scene. The Ruby and Emerald Bazaar covers at least one hundred thousand feet of square footage; has large chunks of ruby and emerald embedded in the saffron stucco that lines the exterior of the bazaar; stained windows with murals of conquest, commerce, and innocence embed the walls; and hundreds of shops teem with life and prosperity within the shelter and some shops that line the bazaar's exterior. The merchants sell and barter diverse items relevant to their trades such as artwork, multi-colored rugs with rare pigments, richly-colored attire fit for the nobility throughout the continent of Lantheon, an official Fropilé bank, woodworks, bakeries and other varying cookeries, and a few smithies that are in the exterior shops of the bazaar.

Among the smithies occupying the exterior shops of the Ruby and Emerald Bazaar is one that has differentiating armor and weapons displayed. Some of the armors have engraved patterns with different colors, animal-like appearances for some sets, and some armor sets blend well with the displayed decorative weaponry. A plump bronzed man with large arms who is wearing a sleeveless and hooded leather tunic, has a thick black beard with snow-white frosting, short black hair with white sides, russet eyes, and has a marigold battle axe engraved with ivory gorillas growling holstered upon his back hammers some heated steel placed atop an anvil next to his forge and kiln. Abelot approaches the counter, yet the blacksmith has his back turned towards the counter as he focuses solely on his work.

Bing! Bing! "Good evening, fellow Master Blacksmith." The man stops hammering and turns towards Abelot. "I noticed your impressive work, but I'm here in Fropilé on diplomatic matters. My ship captain and I need an official escort to the-to the Regemarce to speak with your r-ruler. Do you know of anyone that could assist me?"

The blacksmith completely stops moving and stares directly into Abelot's eyes. "I recognize your face and that hilt on ye blade. Do you mind showing me your sword? My name is Cahít Andíno, and I make the highest quality armor and weapons in Fropilé, with such great quality that even the emperor's Sanguine Guard use my steel," the blacksmith states with a profound husky accent. "They contract their unique orders to me instead of requesting that I permanently stay at or near the Regemarce. I get a lot more business here than I would providing for solely the Etauq Empire."

Abelot unsheathes Morning Glory and hands it to Cahít as the sword shines with magnificence. Cahít Andíno examines the bastard blade.

"This is Morning Glory, and many moons ago I sold that bastard sword to a wealthy lord from Starkton named Peter Wyvern. I also sold him a rapier named Midnight's Arrogance."

Abelot stares into emptiness dumbstruck, and then upon Cahít as Abelot's smile widens. "Peter W-Wyvern is my father. I'm his son Abelot Wyvern. I also have two siblings named Richard and Sable. R-Richard holds Midnight's Arrogance."

"Do you see my dark crimson and ultramarine bastard blade with the orange gorilla head pommel hanging on the wall?"

Abelot looks at the most prominent sword that hangs on one of the walls behind the blacksmith's counter, which happens to be a dark crimson bastard sword with a deep cobalt fuller, ultramarine V-shaped stripes that line the blade, a marigold gorilla head pommel, and golden quillons curved towards the onyx-black grip. "That is the sibling to Morning Glory, and its name is Hadlia. I named them both after flowers that grow in Fropilé and throughout the province of Tavuk." Cahít Andíno examines Morning Glory again. "Ye take good care of 'er edges." He then returns Morning Glory to Abelot.

"Thank you for the observation. So, can you help me and my ship captain, Starkton's Naval Master Tyrian Sterling?"

"Of course, but it will be a while before I can actually assist you since I still have a lot of weapons and armor that need to be made for my clientele."

"I can help."

"You sure? Do you even know how to alter the armor like I do, with the designs and colors embedded into the metal? I noticed that your armor is *gilded* instead of actually embedded with *real gold.*"

"*I'm willing to learn.* I can forge tough steel."

Abelot enters the smithy, removes his chest armor and Morning Glory's holster and places the equipment in a corner, then assists Cahít Andíno with making his unique equipment while Cahít mentors him the entire time. Three hours pass, and there's a lot of ornate equipment cooling. As the sweat-drenched blacksmiths are working, Tyrian Sterling approaches the counter with the books used as evidence of the attack in Starkton with him.

"What the bloody hell are you doing working with this blacksmith, Abelot?"

Cahít Andíno looks upon the confused captain. "You must be the captain this man mentioned earlier. My name is Cahít Andíno, and I make the equipment for Septimius' Sanguine Guard. He's agreed to help me fulfill my orders in exchange for a reliable escort to the capitol. He's doing well for being my apprentice even though his armor is gilded instead of truly gold." Cahít then whispers "What he doesn't know yet is that I'm also willing to sell him a book filled with my techniques so he can improve his equipment quality once you both return to Starkton. I sold his father Morning Glory and Midnight's Arrogance."

"Thank you for deeds on behalf of Starkon and the kingdom's finest blacksmith Abelot, Cahít. Once you and Abelot are finished with the work, I'll be either supervising the crew throughout the Ruby and Emerald Bazaar or visiting one of the brothels close by."

Another hour passes, and the blacksmiths' workload is finally finished after the sun's white-lit morning has transformed into a golden afternoon.

"Cahít, before we leave, I'd like to buy that topaz kukri dagger for my sister. How much is it?" Abelot points his right hand towards a kukri dagger hanging on a wall, which has a topaz blade encrusted with silver swirls and a magenta grip.

"Betrothal to your sister Sable."

Abelot's face tenses. "No."

"Four-hundred gold. Her name is Eloquence. Relax, and learn to take a joke. I'll also sell a book of my techniques for an additional one-hundred gold."

Abelot's face softens. "Done." Abelot removes some gold from his coinpurse and gives it to Cahít. Cahít gives Abelot Eloquence and a smithing book filled with Cahít's techniques, then locks the smithy as Abelot holsters the kukri dagger on his right hip. The blacksmiths get some food and wine from a nearby bakery and wine vendor and eventually find Tyrian Sterling examining some fine garments.

"Maybe my brother needs to give *you* some credible financial mentoring besides just your brother," Abelot chimes at the waffling captain.

"You're right. Let's get to the Regemarce before Septimius is done 'emperor-ing' for the day."

During the men's walk to the Regemarce, they sparsely converse until they are near the palace.

"Abelot, I'm glad that you got some excellent credible mentoring from Cahít today. *Credible mentoring will compliment your success with whatever you need guidance in*," Tyrian proudly states.

"Captain Sterling, you should teach me how to sail sometime. I usually travel horseback," Cahít claims. "Also, what is this meeting about?"

"Remind me sometime and I will. We can't state what happened in Starkton yet until we look Emperor Septimius in the eye. *It's that serious.*"

Cahít looks worried as he, Abelot, and Tyrian walk into the emperor's palace. The great hall is completely made of white marble with grey contours despite having a colorful exterior. The Sanguine Guard and *green guards* are positioned facing each other while protecting the great hall's central path. There is a large marble throne on higher floor space and three doorways behind the thrones, with one of them having stairs that go upward. No one is sitting in the throne, yet a meek man stands near the stairs before the thrones. He approaches Abelot, Tyrian, and Cahít.

"Good evening, Cahít. How may I assist you today?"

Cahít responds with, "we need to speak with Emperor Septimius at once, for these two men are from Starkton on diplomatic business."

The servant nods and then goes through the doorway that has stairs going upward. He returns shortly with an olive-skin man with lustrous black hair wearing an olive-branch crown and burgundy and gold armor, accompanied with a bronzed woman with curly sun-gilt copper hair and hazel eyes wearing a gilded ivory dress with a gilded emerald hooded cloak pinned with a moonstone and gold dragonhead brooch. All three of the men bow once Septimius stands before them.

"You may rise." Cahít, Abelot, and Tyrian stand back up. "Good evening, newcomers. I am Emperor Septimius, and this woman with me is Queen Carillon Doran of Pylon and Daughter of Queen Mother Agnes Doran. You asked for me, Cahít?"

"These men sailed all the way from Starkton to speak with you about diplomatic matters."

"Good evening, Your Majesty. My name is Tyrian Sterling and I am Starkton's Naval Master, captain of my man o' war *Silver Hare*, and the brother of Starkton's King Gwayne Sterling. The man beside me is Abelot Wyvern, Starkton's best blacksmith and brother of Starkton's Treasurer Richard Wyvern. Over a month ago Starkton was attacked by some catspaws that were posing as merchants sailing the merchant galley *The Water Phoenix*, which we sailed with us to Fropilé. We found a manifest and captain's log that state they sailed from Pylon with sand vipers and made a stop here in Fropilé to acquire Tavukish mountain vipers to use in the attack." Tyrian looks at the servant. "Please give Emperor Septimius this evidence." The servant grabs the incriminating books and gives them to Emperor Septimius, which Septimius then rapidly scans, with a darkened expression. Tyrian looks upon Carillon Doran. "We were attacked near Pañase by some pirates, and when the last survivor was interrogated, he said they were following the orders of a woman wearing a green hooded cloak. Emperor Septimius, I strongly advise that you take that woman beside you into custody until her innocence or guilt is determined by your legal system."

"I shall take this seriously due to the evidence that has been provided. Guards, arrest her!" The Sanguine Guard surrounds the woman while the green guards face them with their weapons drawn.

"It's folly to think that I won't be arrested without a fight, for I know that you will wrongfully execute me because my dragon-god Dubuver told me in a dream, and that's his main way of giving me guidance and wisdom. My powerful brother Mace in Honet won't allow my death either. Guards, kill them all."

As Carillon's personal Queen's Guard begin their attack, Emperor Septimius is shielded by two Sanguine Guards while the rest fight the Queen's Guard alongside Cahít, Tyrian, and Abelot. *Kkiissshhhh!* Cahít severs a Pylon Queen's Guard's arm, quickly knocks away another one's spear and then headbutts him in the nose and jaw. Tyrian notices that the suspect is attempting to flee.

"Abelot, get that bitch or everything that we dealt with up to now will be for nothing!" Abelot sprints after her, but realizes that he can't reach her in time, so he unsheathes his new kukri dagger Eloquence then throws it at her. Blood spews from where Carillon's spine is at on the back of her neck as Eloquence impales her neck and she falls facedown onto the floor, unable to move. Several Sanguine and Pylon guards lie dead upon the blood-soaked marble floor as the last remaining Pylon guards in the Regemarce are immediately taken into custody.

"Even though you men are mostly strangers, I appreciate you showing my lesser queen's true nature and incrimination. I will do whatever I can to ensure that Starkton and her people get the justice they deserve."

Abelot looks into Septimius' eyes. "We anticipated to leave with at least one facilitator's head, and it's evident that she had guilt and tried to escape her fate, so we should take her head with us back to Starkton."

"I will allow that. Also, I do need to confiscate *The Water Phoenix* since it is evidence of her crimes."

Tyrian chimes, "it's yours," while Abelot decapitates Carillon Doran's lifeless carcass.

"Cahít, you have helped me in many ways, friend. Thank you."

"You're welcome. I knew she had been deceived by the demon-god Dulcimort the moment she mentioned his alternate name Dubuver, which he answers to by his idiot followers." Cahít nods, then he and the Starkton travelers leave the Regemarce covered in enemy blood.

Near the Regemarce, the older bronzed woman that Abelot passed on his way to the Ruby and Emerald Bazaar pulls back her mantle's hood, only to reveal that she is wearing a gilded green hooded cloak under the mantle instead of a green scarf, along with a gemstone-encrusted bow and dagger.

SEVEN: DEBT

I wonder how Abelot is faring out in the Elysium with Tyrian. Has it actually been over two months since they left?

Snowflakes descend from the heavens outside as Richard stares into empty wall-space near the window. His desk is cluttered with the financial record books of Gwayne Sterling and The White-Grey Keep, a sealed letter Richard scribed, and paper designated for writing letters and taking notes. A high quality oak table with oak chairs that Richard made sits in a corner of the room with carpentry blueprints laying all over it. The remainder of the chamber is meticulously organized, including the bed which now has better quality bedcovers and is deftly dressed. Midnight's Arrogance, sheathed within its scabbard, rests in the holster at Richard's left hip. Richard is holding a rolled letter wrapped with the Wyvern family's orange stamp. Richard unseals the letter he is holding and examines it.

"Dear Richard, As you have requested during your absence, I have been managing your assets just as you have bidden. It's nice seeing all of this money being conveyed unto us. However, I have an inquiry. I have noticed that there is a tremendous sum of debts that has accrued throughout time, relevant to Starkton Trade Company and the rent houses. When could we pay the debt off so your businesses could become more profitable? I know you're better with financial management than I since you're now the Treasurer of The King and The White-Grey Keep. Sincerely, Your Sister Sable Wyvern."

One month after the Elysium catspaws attacked Starkton, Richard hired his sister Sable to manage Starkton Trade Company even though she has already been managing Richard's rental properties due to Richard's exigent necessity of improving Gwayne Sterling's finances as well as that of The White-Grey Keep became more stressful after the violence on Starkton. The tension of maintaining the financial well-being of King Gwayne Sterling, The White-Grey Keep, Richard Wyvern's landlord endeavor, Starkton Trade Company, Richard and Abelot's investment in Alysse's Brothel, and Starkton's recovery after the attack has been festering amongst everyone working with and on behalf of Richard. Richard, during the meager leisure time he gets, works on his carpentry skills by constructing woodworks on some days during the week, hones his swordplay in the training grounds once every two weeks when he is not doing woodworking, and reads after business hours around dusk.

A Lord's Treasure

I need to deliver my official will also. Inspired by Sable's inquiry, Richard Wyvern records some financial aspects that need to be conferred with Gwayne Sterling. He then rolls the parchment, places it on top of his will, pins his white dragon brooch onto his saffron fur doublet, then proceeds towards King Gwayne Sterling's master quarters. As he walks towards the chamber, Richard distantly hears Gwayne's baritone speech reverberating from the great hall.

As Richard passes into The White-Grey Keep's great hall, he sees that King Gwayne is speaking with some exquisitely garbed men. The silver hare of the Sterlings is emblazoned onto his snow-white fur coat. The sundry gazes at Richard Wyvern with silence as he begins to look upon Gwayne Sterling, who appears concerned.

"Your Grace, I have been seeking you. Who are these men?"

"We are here to speak with King Sterling on private matters," chimes a slender bald-headed man with a pointed and frosted copper beard, hazel eyes, emerald and claret cloak with topaz dragon brooch, and maroon doublet. A sheathed dagger and longsword hang from his hips. He chews on mint leaves, causing him to radiate a minty aroma. "Now, if you don't mind-"

"I need to speak with Gwayne about significant matters as well. My name is Richard Wyvern and I'm his personal Treasurer and the Treasurer of The White-Grey Keep."

Gwayne stares at Richard with a worried look on his face.

"Well, it seems to me like you should participate in our discussion. I am Mace Doran from Honet's capital bank and these men standing here with me are from competing financial institutions, including some from Starkton. We're here to discuss Gwayne Sterling's debts."

"How coincidental, me too," Richard states with astonishment.

"It has come to our attention that King Gwayne has been repaying his arrears with loans from various banks, as well as foregoing some payments, and debts that he cosigned are defaulting. If he continues down this financial path, then eventually he will face ruin."

"I am well aware. I can assure you that after the counsel he will receive today from myself as well as your input, there will be great improvements made towards ensuring Gwayne's relationship with the banks, as well as the relationship between Starkton and the banks, remains strong. Certainly we can come to some arrangements."

Mace Doran looks at Richard with slight content, attempting to mask disgust. "Splendid. Our client needs to avoid catastrophic failure if the wellbeing of his family, as well as The White-Grey Keep's wellbeing, is to continue."

"Be glad that I understand your statement just now wasn't a threat to The King Of Starkton and Castellan Of The White-Grey Keep," Richard states as he leers into the banker's eyes with malice on his face. "I do not appreciate your facial expressions and tone."

"I apologize if I have unintentionally made you both feel threatened," the startled banker states as he glances at Gwayne, then to Richard.

A Lord's Treasure

Everyone turns towards King Gwayne as he sits with a worried guise and a golden chalice crusted with emeralds in his left hand. Gwayne sips wine from the chalice as Abelot clears his throat.

"Your Grace, you have entrusted me with helping you with your financial situation, and I am truly trying to assist you. However, there are still some habits that you engage in that you need to cease and desist immediately, and only you can make the necessary choices. I'm proud of the progress that we have gotten done thus far since the situations for you and The White-Grey Keep are getting better, yet I am concerned with the debts that you have acquired. They mostly originate from the extravagant lifestyle that you live."

Gwayne slowly nods.

"You've cared more about living lavishly with falsehood than how to actually live the life that you *feel entitled to* as the most powerful man of this kingdom. You need to stop paying for luxuries through acquiring more debt instead of paying for luxuries that you can actually afford, and quit cosigning debts."

No, Dubuver couldn't have led me astray. Gwayne sips some wine. "I know that you have debt too, Richard," Gwayne exacerbates with retaliation.

Frustration with Gwayne's witticism consumes Richard's emotions. "Yes, I admit that I have debts to pay as well, but my debts are completely different than what you've accumulated. My debt from my studies at Zenith Mountain University gave me financial leverage to be able to pay for the education as well as allow me to get the education I needed to make myself have more valuable knowledge and wisdom that can be applicable for gainful employment. I studied only practical studies that can create value for myself and society instead of studying for the pedigree. I also have business debt, mostly from my shipping company and some mortgages for a few of my rent houses, but that debt has exponentially *amplified* my income so much that I *still* refuse to want any income from this Treasurer position more than two gold coins annually. *The only three debts that anyone could ever need as leverage for success are student loans, business debt, and mortgages. Debt accumulated based upon one's lifestyle is not doing any favors to them, but instead to the lender. Cosigning for loans is folly as well.*"

As Gwayne turns his ashamed face away from Richard, he looks upon Mace as Mace claims, "Even though us bankers greatly appreciate the interest from loan payments, your treasurer is correct in his knowledge of utilizing debt as leverage and the unnecessary risk of cosigning loans."

"Your Grace, do you now see the difference between accruing debt from living a lifestyle you cannot afford and using debt as leverage for building wealth? You need to adequately balance living in the long-term and living in the present when building wealth, and with life in general. It's possible to still live the lifestyle that you want with the money that you and your wife Alysse receive as income, along with what both of you have saved and continue to reserve, but you don't need unnecessary debt to live like that. Cosigning your debts also isn't doing any good since the cosigned borrowers can easily default, and two people will be having financial issues instead of just one."

Damn that god-forsaken dragon dream. Gwayne's mismatched eyes begin to water while he frowns. "I see your point now, Richard. I was blind to the truth for so long that I didn't even think about how I could devastate the endless potential cash flow for The White-Grey Keep and the Sterling family if I keep up my pattern. I promise to implement the needed changes as soon as possible, and to actually follow your guidance, Richard. This I swear upon my son Drake's life."

Mace and the other financiers watch as Gwayne finishes drinking his wine with marine eyes.

"Treasurer, I don't know if we need to continue counseling him at this point, but we still need to review the accounts soon. Thank you for your full cooperation. If he actually improves soon, then he and The White-Grey Keep will remain in good standing with all of us. Let's give King Gwayne a moment to regain his composure"

"You're welcome, Mace Doran."

As the bankers are leaving The White-Grey Keep's great hall, Richard gives the written financial guidelines to Gwayne and then gives him the will. Once Richard leaves Gwayne to meditate on the counsel, and regain his composure, Richard goes outside into the snow-covered courtyard. Starkton's sky is sapphire-blue with snow-white cirrus clouds and innumerable tumbling snowflakes. Mace is nearby, sedentary on a dry bench under the overhanging roof of the bakery recording notes, chewing on mint leaves as he is writing. Smoke billows from the bakery's chimney. The mixing aromas of mint, bread, peach pie, blueberry pie, and wood smoke fill the air as Richard walks toward Mace, soaking his shoes and the bottom of his pants with the snow's condensation.

"Mister Doran, do you still wish to converse with me about Gwayne's accounts?"

Mace's hazel eyes sparkle as he changes his focus from the writings on his lap to Richard's position. "Of course, I wish to help you improve King Gwayne Sterling's finances as well as that of The White-Grey Keep."

"Very well. Let us begin, but in warmth. I'm also hungry."

"Agreed."

Richard and Mace enter The White-Grey Keep's balmy, aromatic bakery. Five bakers are working with the ovens and organizing the baked goods, filling the display counter shelves. Richard orders a peach pie and a Starkton sweet red while Mace orders a blueberry pie and mint cookies with white zinfandel. The men sit at a nearby table and enjoy their meal while conversing.

"Wyvern, huh? I remember doing business with your forefathers Peter and Cedric. Isn't Leggeron your grandfather?"

"Indeed Leggeron the Stern, the greatest sellsword to ever work in and around Starkton, is my grandfather. He actually got his name from when my great grandparents went to Greca or Namor, whichever city or country it was, and noticed the statues that were erected for the most noteworthy gods and goddesses of whatever religion they practice. He got his Stern title from not being the kindest person to ruffians and literally being stern about his pricing. My brother Abelot has a lot in common with Leggeron, and I wish Leggeron was still alive to spend time with him. I keep forgetting which polytheistic religion Leggeron got his name from because both places have a similar religion with different deity names and I follow the One True God Veritamor."

Mace sips his wine. "Allow me to correct you, Lord Wyvern. Namor is the capital of Greca, and I'm surprised that you've forgotten this fact since Greca borders the Starkton province. I remember when Leggeron walked into my bank accusing me of cheating his sons with excessive interest on their business loans. He slew three guards that dared to attack him, disemboweling them before my very eyes, as a warning not to provoke the Wyvern family ever again. *I responded by informing him that threatening me is not wise, for I am a younger brother of Queen Carillon Doran in Pylon.*"

Richard's eyes widen. "You're a prince? Why the feck are not in Pylon ruling?"

"I don't want to be seen as an entitled shit like most nobility and wanted to make my own success. I'm now one of the most powerful men in Lantheon."

Both men continue eating, with Richard finishing his peach pie while most of Mace Doran's blueberry pie is gone. Richard sips his sweet red wine.

"Now, let's get to business. Show me the accounts."

"How do you propose that Gwayne should handle his debts?"

"What's worked for me in the past, when I accrued educational debt with multiple loans, is that I eliminated the smallest loan as quickly as possible while paying minimal payments on the larger debts. Once the smallest loan was gone, I did the same thing with the next smallest debt but saved the money that would have gone towards the previous debt. Some people actually stack the debt payments after a debt is paid, but that eliminates the ability to save more money. I never went broke."

"Indeed I have witnessed clients stack their debt payments to pay down some debts quicker, but I too personally prefer to stow the gold that went to the lower payments even though more interest will be paid over time. Whichever choice one prefers is the one they will practice. *Debt used as leverage is money that you simply owe and not necessarily don't possess.* Make sure that King Gwayne knows our wisdom about debt and the two effective amortization methods we acknowledge."

"It was written on some parchment I gave to him earlier before I went outside and met with you."

Richard examines the account book to verify that Gwayne has a dire situation, only for Mace to briefly interrupt him.

"Would you like to finish the rest of my wine?"

"Yes, of course. I've been dealing with a lot of stress lately also."

Mace's eyes sparkle as Richard reaches for the glass and drinks the wine. After Richard finishes Mace's wine for him, they both leave the bakery only to hear some commotion outside of the building near the great hall. Five wagons are tipped over while ten assailants in *emerald-green* attire and masks, wielding scimitars, fight against some of the guards. Mace and Richard join in the fight. Richard rushes up to one of the assailants and impales him through his back and heart with Midnight's Arrogance, yet another gets a deep thrust between Richard's right ribs. Blood blankets the white earth from the fallen assailant and Richard's wound. Richard quickly challenges him and parries his blade as the assailant extends forward and Richard quickly stabs him through his throat. Two assailants remain standing. One of the assailants rushes around a guard and slices the guard's throat after he passes. Mace and Richard then team up together to finish the assailant, but as they both charge at the assailant he impales Richard through his navel. The guards quickly eliminate the final assailant before they can cause any further devastation.

Mace Doran notices Richard's pale skin, mortal wounds, and bloodstained garments.

"Richard, we need to get you medical attention right away! Guards, find a doctor and King Gwayne!"

Chaos lingers amongst The White-Grey Keep's courtyard as the inhabitants panic from the attack and the guards search for someone to help Richard and locate the king. Richard's dark burgundy lifeblood saturates the ivory slush as his skin becomes as pale as the snow, the color of his eyes' violet flakes fades away, and his lips turn as purple as Abelot's Morning Glory. Reality begins to fade away.

Richard walks a path amidst the edifices of Zenith Mountain University, with a bag full of books shielding his back. He carries a fat sack of gold on his waist, he has a full head of hair, beautiful female students walking past take glances at he and his coinpurse, and the weather is fair yet chilled. As he is heading to the university's library, snowflakes begin to slowly blanket the earth. *"Richard!"* He locates a seat on the dimly lit quietest floor that overlooks the other students and begins to study after lighting a candle for visibility. *The Prosperous Lord.* As he is studying, an older man almost identical to Richard, but with grey hair and sapphire eyes, walks over to him and sits down nearby.

"Do you remember me?" Richard lifts his gaze to meet the man's. *"Pl-Please don't die on me, Richard."*

"Yes, I do, Father. Or do you prefer Peter?"

Peter Wyvern's look slightly tenses. "I'd prefer that you do well with your life and that you continue studying. Have you paid back your loans yet?"

"Fetch him some water and get him on the wagon! He's still bleeding everywhere. Do you not know how to put on tourniquets properly?!" "I intend to be as successful as I can become with my life, and I have realized that to reach this goal I cannot follow the advice and demands of those who live in misery and poverty due to foolish decision-making and no true desire to live well. I hope you're proud."

The world becomes an endless darkness, until light becomes visible once again.

EIGHT: SELF-EMPLOYMENT

How much gross profit is the expedition to the Elysium provinces expected to attain for myself and Starkton Trade Company?" Sable asks Marigold Bilteen in Starkton Trade Company's snow-covered edifice near the Starkton wharf as she stops strumming her silver harp and stares into Marigold's purpureus eyes. Sable is wearing a fuchsia samite bodice lined with an ermine collar emphasizing her cleavage and has her copper hair pulled back into a bundle of curls while Marigold is wearing a much more subtle ivy array and fox-pelt cloak.

"My Lady, please don't disremember Abelot's imbursement as well as the payout for the labor and the merchants that commissioned our services. Plus or minus a few gold, it is still expected to be a tremendous amount according to the books here at the office. I hate that you're acquiring ownership over this profitable venture from Richard's death. Again, I'm sorry for your loss."

Sable's eyes begin to fill with tears. "Richard's legacy shall prolong amid Abelot's success and mine own, and you will warrant that expectation through your servitude to the Wyverns. Thank you. You're performing excellently as Starkton Trade's newest manager. Abelot will be forlorn when he learns about Richard's undeserved bereavement." Streams flow down Sable's cheeks. "What news of the aggressors?"

"So far, the general belief is that they are connected to the ones that devastated Starkton over two months ago. They have similar weaponry, their clothing is of the same style, and the items that were found in the wagons were similar to what was found on *The Water Phoenix*, but there were no snakes. The attackers were possibly trying to assassinate Gwayne Sterling, and possibly some other high-ranking lords and ladies, but they were only able to get to your brother Richard and a few guards. Hopefully Captain Sterling and Abelot will have more answers, justice on behalf of the victims, and the anticipated profit from trade."

Common folk and a few nobility traverse through the snow-covered streets past the office going to the docks yet others go elsewhere. Snow tumbles from a grey sky. A fur-covered alchemist under a maroon-wooded overhang nearby sells potions and herbs to both the sick and healthy from his large table covered with herbs, mortar-and-pestles, alembics, retorts, potions, and empty labeled bottles. A nearby jester, wearing green and purple motley, dances while performing tricks, with some occasional slips, for his crowd as they slide gold into his brown clay vase. Even though the common folk people spend their money as they choose, they still do not display any true signs of wealth, for their clothes are mostly ragged and bland. The adults and children alike are unbathed and reek of excretions and body odor. The majority of the commoners appear malnourished enough to expose bones under the skin, and most of everything they pay for is cheap and of low quality. The people have little free time due to many hours of low-pay labor, and some of these people are even barefoot. The nobility don boots and fur-lined cloaks atop their richly-colored attire while some wear dyed fur coats, harshly shoving opulence in the faces of the common folk through the lavish appearance of the lifestyles of the nobility and merchants.

Sable stares out of Starkton Trade's entrance upon the poor with disgust. "Why do the common folk of Starkton deliberately choose poverty over riches *and* freedom?"

"What do you mean, Lady Wyvern? These people are basically getting their wants and needs and some are currently spending their time being entertained by the jester."

"Don't be angry with my inconvenient wisdom I have to say, but it is a brutal truth. What I meant was that they are slaves to the idea that mindlessly working for meager income from a single payer will gain them the riches they could attain from being fairly paid by many people. They are nobodies when being compared to their employers and nobility. Look at their rags, skinny and unhealthy bodies, and poverty! I used to spend most of my time during the week dealing with tenants on behalf of Richard, but now that *I am expecting to successfully practice self-employment, I now have a lot of free time and wealth* since I now have you working on my behalf and you actually enjoy interacting with those unfortunate ignorami. *Richard spent a lot of time upfront trying to be successful with self-employment, and he made his landlord endeavor so successful that he was able to hire me to do most of the work for him after a while and created free time for himself while he started to rise closer to royalty.* I am thankful for the sacrifices that he made since I have partially inherited his livelihood."

"Lady Wyvern, please remember to stay humble as much as possible since customers of all the ventures you inherited do give you their money to rent the houses, manage the exportation and importation logistics, and engage in all of the filth at Alysse's Brothel," Marigold anxiously responds with a reddened face.

"I actually forgot about the brothel's income. With all of these income sources through self-employment, I think I will enjoy my new life. I bet that Abelot's getting even more money since he has more income streams than I thanks to his smithy."

"Sable, remember that sometimes you need to review the progress of the businesses since the success of the businesses is ultimately your responsibility even though I operate Starkton Trade Company and engage the tenants on you and Abelot's behalf."

Grung! Grung! Large brass bells rigorously reverberate throughout Starkton, with a deafening concentration in the wharf, which draws a crowd to congregate amidst the harbor. Naval Master Tyrian Sterling's *Silver Hare* and seven frigates are spotted docking at their respective berths, yet *The Water Phoenix* is nowhere to be seen.

An oaken horse-drawn carriage pulled by a white mare and filly is spotted heading in the direction of the wharf while Sable rushes to the docks to check on the presumable arrival of her brother Abelot and Tyrian Sterling. Sable slips and falls, but gets back up with a wet dress. As *Silver Hare*'s ramp is lowered from the deck, more people crowd around the docks, and then Captain Sterling and Abelot Wyvern begin to descend towards the snow-covered dock. Both men have a ragged appearance thanks to Tyrian's unkempt black coat and Abelot's unkempt beard, yet Abelot holds a yellowish object in his right hand and a book under his left arm. The oak carriage parks behind the crowd and opens to reveal King Gwayne Sterling wearing a hare-pelt coat, who walks through the snow to the dock to reunite with his brother and his former Treasurer's siblings. Abelot and Tyrian advance towards the crowd, which parts for Gwayne Sterling and Sable Wyvern who are approaching them. The crowd gives a solemn silence.

"Good evening, dear sister and King Gwayne. How fares Starkton and her people?"

"Abelot, there is something important I must tell you. A week ago there was an attack on the castle, and Richard was overwhelmed and bled to death from his mortal wounds. Marigold Bilteen informed me about the attackers possibly being linked to the ones from a few months ago due to some similarities noted between the assailants from both attacks." Sable cries.

King Gwayne Sterling bears a funereal face as he states "I am sorry for your loss, Abelot."

Abelot's face tenses as he briefly looks down to the right. Abelot's voice cracks as he asks, "If Richard's dead, then who is the new Treasurer?"

Gwayne solemnly responds with, "I sent a letter to High King Lesirion in the gold and ivory city of Honet about what happened, and he promptly responded and sent Mace Doran of Honet Bank to act as the new Treasurer."

Abelot's eyes widen with his furrowed brows. "I guess Mace will loathe my existence once you send him his sister Carillon's severed head." Abelot holds up the head towards Gwayne.

The citizens notice Carillon Doran's head, which triggers an eruption of rambunctious celebration on behalf of Starkton's unrightfully deceased victims. Abelot gives the severed head to Gwayne Sterling.

"King Gwayne, I will let you and Sable converse with Tyrian. I need to get back to-to my smithy and get used to working with the-with the new techniques I learned in Fropilé. I'm glad that I'm self-employed and don't have to let someone above me take my expected profit growth for themselves while giving me barely anything for my labor. This crowd is bothering me, and so is my currently filthy body."

"You're not going back to the smithy just yet, Abelot, whether or not you are clean. You're riding with me to the castle, so

I can properly bestow you the property ownership that Richard willed to you. Your sister has already received hers."

NINE: QUALITY

*B*ing! Bing! Bing!

Snow has long since stopped falling, yet the air is still chilled and Starkton's less traversed ground remains overlaid with defrosting snow. Abelot's smithing hammer slams against blistering orange-red steel atop his smithy's anvil as lords, sellswords, and knights observe his toil and its results. Abelot's Smithy is a smithy elongated back far enough to soften noises from the outside world to ensure he doesn't have to struggle with receiving too much stimuli. A neat-bearded Abelot is working with his hair pulled back into a ponytail, and he's wearing golden armor with saffron ripples flowing all over like water, no vambraces or pauldrons, an ivory dragon in the center of the breastplate, and matching wings on the back piece. His enclosed dragon head helmet lies in a back corner next to his bastard sword Morning Glory, vambraces, and pauldrons. Nearby Abelot's Smithy, Sable plays her harp in angelic harmony alongside Marigold's lute for the growing crowd at their platform. *Distraction from the harsh reality of all who have fallen from the attacks on Starkton and the harsh living conditions of Starkton's beggars and poor during the winter.* Several of Sable's crowd members are drunk and holding empty wine bottles. There are gold coins laying all over the front of the platform, and Abelot's Smithy is full of vibrantly tinted armors and weaponry. Some of the knights outside the smithy remain perched upon their opulently steel-clad steeds, and the mercenaries wear varying armors and weaponry relevant to their fighting style.

Clip Clap Clop. Clip Clap Clop. Clip Clap Clop. Riding towards Abelot's Smithy is General Randall Bilteen in freshly fashioned burgundy and marigold ornate armor with the Bilteen fox head on the center of the cuirass, a burgundy and marigold fox head helmet with a golden mail gorget, fox head-shaped shoulder pauldrons, and fox paw-shaped gauntlets. On his hip is a large sack of gold and a sealed envelope with the Sterling seal pinned onto the sack. Randall's silver stallion drops steaming dung in the road as he walks, which soon after an oblivious passerby steps into. Randall's stallion is also sporting crimson and marigold armor, with its chanfron having a foxlike appearance.

"Good evening, Abelot. I noticed your smithy has been much more successful than it ever was since you returned from your voyage to Fropilé. You've always *avoided mediocrity* when crafting your wares, and you have definitely improved the quality through your new techniques. I greatly enjoy my new armor and the armor on my steed, so expect a visit from my sons Rickard and Robert." Randall removes the large pouch of gold and attached letter from his belt and tosses them into Abelot's left hand. "In that envelope is the measurements of every member of King Gwayne's personal guard, and the gold is to handsomely pay you for the armor. I suggest you begin working on it once you have the time to do so. You're making your family proud. I wouldn't be surprised if the king ever decides to make you the first Master Blacksmith to guarantee you work and pay by focusing solely on the crown's demands. Lordship has its perks... and constraints."

"I'm already a master blacksmith, but not a lo'd. I'd rather make money by serving *everyone* high quality gear rather than solely our king. The quality of everything you-you-you-you... *the quality of everything you do can determine whether or not you gain opulence or experience poverty through avoidance.* I'm richer by serving as many people as possible at once rather than solely one person."

"Understood. Master Blacksmith would most likely be your lordship title though, if King Gwayne ever decides to make you nobility just like your brother."

"I'm also a skilled sellsword. I sometimes have to escort, protect, and confront people for pay."

"*I know.*" Randall nods and then rides towards Sable and Marigold's platform.

General Bilteen listens to the music, yet stares onward upon his beautiful daughter Marigold as she plays her lute. Everyone

besides Marigold and Sable are quiet, yet the only noises being heard
are whispers amongst the crowd, a drunkard in the crowd retching,
gold being tossed onto the platform, Abelot's hammer molding steel,
noises caused by livestock and wildlife, and the harmonious sounds
of commerce throughout the metropolis.

An angry drunk starts yelling at another person in the crowd.
"Thief! Give me back the gold you stole!"

"Feck off, dimwit. You threw your gold at the 'bardin" wenches." The
accused thief spits at the angry drunk, and the drunkard swings his
bottle at the men. He breaks his bottle over the suspect, glass shards
vault in all directions, and then the drunkard sweepingly attempts to
attack the unarmed man as he distances himself away from the
belligerent drunk. People surrounding them begin to panic and flee
while some enrage. Broken glass blankets the ground, and some
barefoot beggars get the bottoms of their feet cut open amidst the
erupting chaos. Marigold and Sable's music stops, and so does
Abelot's hammering. Randall jumps off of his horse and rushes
towards the fight. Randall thinks about the worst possible outcome
while shoving people aside.

Some of the people try to pull the angry drunk away, but they
and some other surrounding people get cut, and the violence quickly
escalates. Every crowd member, most notably the heavily
intoxicated, is fighting while several quickly flee. The warriors
surrounding Abelot's Smithy sprint over to the riot and combat the
rioters. Fifty city guards rush over. "Drop your weapons!" The
fighters that were outside Abelot's Smithy sheathe their weapons and

retreat as the guards advance onward while shielding themselves and wielding maces. Many rioters are quickly knocked unconscious while the guards advance towards the center of the riot. Soon every rioter is incapacitated while the guards bind their wrists and grab wagons to load them into to carry towards the castle's dungeon.

As General Bilteen returns to reality, he has already reached the violent drunkard with the broken bottle. The unarmed thievery suspect is at a relatively safe distance away from the quarrelsome drunk. The drunk clumsily slashes at Randall, but misses as Randall retreats. Randall unsheathes has falchion sword. "Put the glass down!" The alcoholic rushes forward, but slips on the burgundy puke puddle and falls face first into it while getting vomit and glass smeared into his clothes from the fall. He acquires numerous cuts on his hands and face. As the drunk rolls onto his back, getting even more cuts in the process, Randall points the tip of his falchion onto his throat directly under his chin.

"Don't even think about getting back up. Guards! Arrest him!" Some city guards arrest the man and restrain him as they stand before General Bilteen. The drunk is covered in blood, cuts, and vomit. "I hereby charge you with assault and battery with a weapon, attempted murder with a deadly weapon, and endangering the public with weaponry. You will be escorted to the dungeon until King Gway-"

Huaahh! The man vomits. Randall Bilteen and some surrounding people back up further away from the man. "You will be escorted to the dungeon unless the king commands otherwise.

Guards, take him to the dungeon. All of you sentinels not escorting him stay." The guards restraining the criminal take him away.

Randall shouts at the surrounding citizens, "everyone in this crowd, give your bottles and weaponry to the guards, then leave." Each one that wields a bottle begins to surrender their bottle to the Starkton guards. Randall looks at Sable and Marigold staring at him and the crowd in shock. "Ladies, I apologize for ending your magnificent performance early, but I believe that you have done well today despite the outbreak of drunken violence. I strongly suggest that you call it a day and hire a lot more security for your next performance." More and more members of the crowd surrender the bottles and other objects they are holding until everyone except the guards and Randall are left standing near the broken glass and vomit. The ladies are gathering the scattered gold as Abelot is walking over to Randall.

"That was quite impressive work you just accomplished. Had you not pacified the situation as efficiently as you did, that could have quickly become a riot."

"I know, Abelot. I envisioned a riot breaking out as I was sprinting towards the violent quarrel. Effectively neutralizing violence is one of my strengths that I use to my advantage as the General of Starkton's Army and Supreme Commander of the Guard. At ease."

Abelot walks back towards his smithy to continue working on his equipment as General Bilteen climbs onto his armored stallion and rides toward the direction of the White-Grey Keep.

Three hours have passed, and the sky has become a banner with a saffron sun on a field of wine, mulberry, and gold. As the sun melts a menial amount of remnant snow, Abelot sustains working until he reaches an appropriate stopping point for the day. Bundles of armor and weapons lie all over Abelot's Smithy, yet Abelot gathers his own equipment instead of allowing it to be mixed with the orders. He then locks the smithy to prevent thievery, and dines at a nearby tavern and brewery called The Prancing Fox. He orders and eats his favorite meal from this tavern, cottage pie topped with mashed potatoes, apples, and The Prancing Fox's popular amber ale as his beverage.

EPILOGUE

I love sweet reds almost as much as my redheaded wife, girl, but I think I have had my fill for now." King Gwayne places his meaty hand over his golden goblet.

She nods. "Yes, Your Grace."

The servant girl quickly pulls back the silver wine pitcher and places it on the table, then walks away from the White-Grey Keep's mess hall table as King Gwayne listens to the hearthfire peacefully crackle and Mace Doran guzzle his Starkton wine. King Gwayne looks at a rolled parchment that he has with him. Not a soul is in the room except for the departing girl, King Gwayne, and the new Treasurer Mace Doran. Mace's beard shines from the fire's light as the flames dance in his hazel eyes.

"Thank you for meeting with me, and obviously showing appreciation for the White-Grey Keep's chefs and wine cellar. However, as you can guess, I did not call you here just to feed you."

Mace Doran finishes his wine. "Indeed this is some succulent venison and a sweet Starkton red. Why have you been drinking Starkton wine lately instead of your usual Iytaleesh?"

"I listened to Richard when he told me that day that I needed to fix my own habits on behalf of my finances and that of Starkton and The White-Grey Keep. This Starkton red is cheaper than my usual Iytaleesh red and has a very similar, sweet flavor." King Gwayne's gaze moves lower right, towards his own goblet. "I also don't drink as often as I did after I saw Richard's lifeless body that very same day. I'm not going to let that loyal man's wisdom he bestowed upon me be wasted in vain."

Mace Doran's eyes sparkle. "I barely knew the man, yet met his grandfather Leggeron many years ago when I was doing business with Richard's father Peter and uncle Cedric. From what I understand Abelot has a lot in common with their grandfather Leggeron whereas Richard had a lot in common their father Peter."

Abelot's a dangerous threat, just like Leggeron. "I was there with Richard when the attack happened, fighting alongside the lord, and I was there with him when his blood soaked the snowy earth."

"Let's stop thinking about the negativity regarding Richard's death. What do you think he thought about, or possibly saw, as he was dying?"

He saw the new Treasurer, you ignoramus. "I've heard from people who claim to have briefly died then resurrected that they saw their lives flash before their eyes in an instant, and I heard from others that they remembered the best moment of their lives. Some people even claim to have ascended to the heavens or descended to the underworld and saw the deities and demons of lore."

"I hope that I remember one of the best moments of my life before I die, and I think one of those memories will be the first time I read the notes Richard made for me. I called you here so I can show you part of his vision for success and let his bestowed guidelines potentially improve your principles." King Gwayne unrolls the parchment. "I have been reading these notes that Richard left over and over again, solely because they changed my life for betterment rather than ruin. *I truly live like a king now rather than an ignorant drunkard.*"

"Well, let's hear his words of wisdom then. He and I briefly discussed some of the things he claimed to have written on that parchment for you, and I would like to hear what all he truly had to say."

King Gwayne Sterling begins to read Richard's financial wisdom aloud.

"*Dear King Gwayne Sterling, I have been serving faithfully as your Treasurer and the Treasurer of Starkton and The White-Grey Keep for roughly about six months now. Even though I have been able to execute improvement for the financial situation of the castle and partially for your wellbeing, my vision for your success has been experiencing hindrance. I have tried to put your financial wellbeing on a right path towards success, yet you continue to engage in the behaviors that have been hindering your wellbeing and the wellbeing of The White-Grey Keep. If you stay true to these principles, then I believe that you will be moving closer towards wealth:*

Saving: Save at least one-fifth, rounded up to the nearest well-rounded hundredth, of all incomes received, and either split it evenly between expansion and reserves or put the money entirely into reserves.

Expenses: Reduce expenses wherever possible while trying to meet middle ground between quality of life and the quantity of resources while living within your finances.

Skills and Education: Always be sharpening your skillset, and master a few skills instead of being mediocre at many. Train your mind, just like the sentries train in the training grounds.

Income: Passive income is an excellent way to build wealth alongside having an active income, and passive income can be acquired through business ownership, collecting rent, writing books, writing plays, and numerous other methods.

Risk Management: Always diversify your risks instead of putting too many resources in one place, for catastrophes can happen.

Mentorship: Credible mentorship can vastly improve one's skills, which can exponentially improve one's income and wellbeing when properly utilized.

Debt: Debt can be used as a leverage to improve the ability to produce income. The only three debts one should have if necessary are student loans, a mortgage, and business debt, and all other debts are folly, especially debts based upon lifestyle. Cosigning debt is utter folly, for both borrowers can be negatively affected by failure. There are two different methods for effective amortization that

I recognize: Stack the debt payments on top of each other to pay off debt much faster after some debts are completely paid, or save the debt payments after some debts have been paid to have more money available. Debt is money that is owed, and not necessarily money that isn't available.

Self-Employment: Self-employment, when practiced properly, is naturally much more profitable than being an employee due to the customers giving direct payment instead of simply receiving a small fraction of the money from an employer. Dependent upon the self-employment situation, either a lot of time can be freed by doing a tremendous amount of labor upfront and profiting from it, or simply have employees do the work instead, or self-employment can preoccupy a lot of time and require tedious labor.

Quality: The quality of one's skills, goods, and services will determine whether or not the person can be rewarded with opulence and warranted attention or burdened with poverty and unwarranted avoidance.

I do my best to practice these principles whenever possible, and following these financial principles has been helping me to achieve my financial goals. You and The White-Grey Keep both have reserved resources, and I reduced some of the expenses for the castle while creating new revenue sources through the moat and the water wheels. I thank you for allowing me to help fix your financial issues and making The White-Grey Keep much more profitable while allowing me to profit from my ventures, for I truly believe that you chose the right man for the responsibility. Sincerely, Your Treasurer Richard Wyvern."

Mace stares into King Gwayne's mismatched eyes with widened eyes and a surprised look upon his face. "Well, I didn't expect to hear the words of financial wisdom from one of Starkton's wealthiest men to say much less about money than I actually expected. I have years of experience working with money and investing due to my time with Honet's bank. Had I been the one to write the letter, I would have discussed investing in financial tools."

"Due to his implementation of the principles he wrote for me, I bet that when he died he was most likely wealthier than you."

"Didn't he leave a lot of gold, rental properties, ownership interest in the Starkton Trade Company and Alysse's Brothel, and some personal belongings to split between his surviving siblings?"

"Yes, he gave me his will before he died. I'm not going to tell you how much gold he gave to Sable and Abelot though."

"Understood. I will definitely think about Richard's wisdom as I strategize your finances and the finances of the castle. Is this all that you wanted to speak with me about, Your Grace?"

King Gwayne's face shows concern. "Pour yourself another serving of wine." Mace obeys the king's command with worry as he pours himself some more Starkton red wine, shaking throughout the entire process. "Are you aware that your sister Carillon, Queen of Pylon, was implied as being guilty of the Starkton attack months ago and ordered her guards to kill Emperor Septimius of the Etauq Empire, Abelot, and my brother Tyrian when she was charged with the evidence?"

Mace shockingly asks, "When is her trial?" as his goblet shakes in his hand. He sips and spills some of the wine onto himself and the table.

"She's dead. She was executed by Abelot when her guards attacked. Abelot brought me her head, which I stored in a box so you could give her a proper funeral. I didn't tell you before now since I didn't want the stress of her death, on top of the stress from your new position as the Treasurer, to devastate your psychological state."

"That ungrateful bastard. I fought alongside his brother when The White-Grey Keep was attacked, and this is how he repays me? Killing my sister instead of letting her have a trial to prove her innocence or guilt about the attack?" Mace's face blackens as tears begin to flow down his cheeks.

"The confrontation happened before the attack on the castle, which had too many similarities to the attack months ago. She should have been charged with it as well, if she lived longer. Also, I'm curious as to why you did not accept the title of Prince Mace instead of being a banker in Honet."

"My older br-brother Davirius decided to remain in Pylon's court while I wanted to impact the world elsewhere. She got precedence over Davirius and I due to the lineage system in the Elysium provinces being based on birth instead of sex."

"Just so we're clear, I will not charge you in her place due to the catspaws trying to kill you as well, so I don't see you as a suspect despite your earlier threat. You're dismissed, and I'm sorry that you had to learn of her death this way and this late."

Good. An upset Mace Doran begins to leave, but just as he is leaving a servant boy approaches King Gwayne with a letter in hand.

King Gwayne looks upon the boy. "Bugger off, ye little shit. Not now."

"I have a message from Emperor Septimius of Tavuk."

King Gwayne's face begins to blacken. "Give it here, and stay." The boy hands him the letter, and King Gwayne promptly reads it. *Worry consumes his emotions.* "Send for my brother Naval Master Tyrian Sterling and Abelot Wyvern immediately. My brother will be at the docks, possibly with his ship *Silver Hare,* and Abelot has a prominent smithy named after himself."

"Yes, Your Grace."

The boy leaves as King Gwayne pours himself some more wine.

David S. Longworth was born in November 1992 and grew up in Elkin, North Carolina. He earned his Bachelor's of Science in Business Administration from Appalachian State University in 2015. David served Appalachian State University's Fencing Team as the team's Public Relations Officer during the spring 2015 semester and wrote informational articles for Club Sports Illustrated. As an entrepreneurial Aspergian, David strives for being an influential role model for people on the Autism Spectrum.

www.twitter.com/longworthd92

62867907R00064

Made in the USA
Middletown, DE
27 January 2018